CARIBBEAN TALE

Rudy Gurley

aCaribbeanTale.com

ISBN 1-4276-0535-1
aCaribbeanTale.com

For information address to Rudy Gurley,
aCaribbeanTale.com, PO Box RB2520,
Rodney Bay Industrial Zone, Gros-Islet, St. Lucia.
Tel: 1–758–450–8035. Email: r.gurley@btinternet.com

Printed in the United States of America

Typeset by Palimpsest Book Production Limited
Grangemouth, Stirlingshire, Scotland

October 2006

Visit our website at www.aCaribbeanTale.com

For Susanna, Roslyn and Sheila

ACKNOWLEDGEMENTS

I'd like to thank my wife, Susanna, who continues to stand beside me like a rock . . . solid and unyielding.

My aunt, Sheila, for continuing to be my mother and father.

My sister, Roslyn, and her husband, Pete, for their encouragement and support from across the Atlantic.

My business manager, Magdalene Charles William, for her commitment and support, and for believing in the project, and in me.

My domestic helper, Virginia, for taking such great care of me, keeping the coffee flowing . . . and the eats too, while I typed away in my study.

My closest friends, Alastair Macdonald of Jamaica, and Ivan Augustine of St. Lucia . . . for their encouragement.

All my other friends and family who, over the past several months, I've had to shun . . . now you know why . . . hope you can forgive me.

Jacques Compton, for his editorial pen and for our debates on the technical aspects of the English language . . . hope you don't think I've gone too far with my Americanisms.

Thanks to Mrs. Macdonald (Alastair's mom) of Jamaica for her guidance. Thanks to Owen Platt and Kate Scane for their help in the very early days.

Thanks to Stephen Paul and Chris Huxley for their brilliant photography.

Many thanks to Pat and Mike at Quebecor World. Thanks also to James at Blacksheep for the excellent cover design.

Thanks to the guys at Palimpsest for their professional typesetting . . . you guys have done for me as great a job as you did for J.K. Rowling of Harry Potter fame.

A million thanks to Caroline Petherick, who came on at the eleventh hour, and who, under extreme pressure, provided an excellent proofreading and editorial service.

A
CARIBBEAN
TALE

CHAPTER 1

London – 1985

They were closing in on me. Police officers . . . their faces stern, heartless.

In the biting, bitter cold, on and on I struggled to run on legs that grew weaker and weaker with every step.

Chilled to the bone, I pulled up against a brick wall, chest heaving, panicked eyes darting wildly around me.

Nowhere to run. Nowhere to hide.

What did I do? I'm innocent! my brain screamed, my heart threatening to burst with each thunderous beat.

Sick with fright, I pressed back hard against the wall, feeling its icy façade raking my flesh, sending ripples of uncontrollable shivers through my core.

God! I'm freezing . . . did I come to London to die like this?

The uniformed men in their domed helmets surrounded me. In their eyes I saw no pity, no mercy . . . only brutal contempt. From behind the swarm

1

of law enforcers, I thought I heard a familiar-sounding voice . . . a throaty cockney accent, bellowing bitterly . . . something about a 'thieving bastard!'

The wall of men with stern, glaring faces parted. Icy chills rippled relentlessly through me.

Then I saw him.

The squat, large-bellied, plaster-white-faced man in a thick overcoat had long, greasy jet-black hair pulled back in a messy pony-tail. His gold tooth sparkled.

Where had I seen that creature before?

My panic-stricken eyes shot down to his gloved hands in which he carried . . . a . . . a bucket?

The man stepped back on short bandy legs, and heaved the bucket. Icy water doused my body – my face, my neck, my chest . . .

"It's freezing!" I screamed.

And with a start I awoke from the nightmare.

I held my chest and heaved a huge sigh of relief, eyes flicking embarrassed glances around the bus.

Almost empty. Thank God.

I blinked and blinked to banish sleep from my eyes. Slowly, the grogginess began to lift, as I sat there in the front row of the big red double-decker bus, numb with cold, shivers shuddering through me.

Then I found the culprit.

Some cheeky person had propped open the glass window over my head. Frigid wind was billowing in through the open space, slamming into me, chilling me to the bone.

Isn't it cold enough already in this big fridge?

I reached up with undisguised disgust, and clamped shut the window.

It escaped me why people insisted on opening bus windows in the dead of winter. *Why on earth?*

Exasperated, I shook my head and slumped back down into the cushioned seat, folding my arms tightly across my chest, shivering, feeling goose bumps erupting over my entire body.

But coldness wasn't my only ailment.

Only minutes before I had hoisted myself up the spiral metal stairs to the back of the bus, ambled down the slatted wooden floor and took my accustomed seat in the front row – a position from which I often viewed the sights of London. At seven fifteen this frigid February morning in 1985, the double-decker bus, outbound from the city, was nearly empty. Just as well, for sight-seeing had been the last thing on my mind.

It occurred to me that I must have dozed soon after boarding, for the bus hadn't yet rounded the corner from Haymarket into Trafalgar Square.

That dream . . . that nightmare, must have come quickly . . . it wasn't the first time . . . it . . .

I shook my head, banishing the thought. *Let it rest.*

I folded my arms tighter across my chest, legs clasped firmly together. Despite my thick winter jacket, and woollen scarf wrapped snugly around my slender neck, my body was a spasm of shivers.

3

Bone-weary and stiff, my body pleaded for sleep, but was kept awake by the deep gloom that overwhelmed me, the dark worries and dismal speculations parading through my wary mind.

What was I thinking, coming to this country in the dead of winter? How will I survive this? What on earth am I doing in this cold city? Why didn't I stay home in the sunshine where I belong?

At twenty-one, I was sufficiently well-read to know that those were questions a good many others had asked on finding themselves marooned in the sometimes impersonal city, in the depths of a bitter English winter.

Cupping my mouth, I yawned long and hard. My mind flashed back to words I had so frequently read in a travel magazine tucked away in my haversack that I'd committed them to memory:

Summer in London could be attractive. The city seems to have ample green spaces for relaxation and the bursts of sunshine, however infrequent, does much to lift the mood of its peoples. But it is a brief respite and, as the days grow shorter and the temperatures fall, the commuters scurry home at the end of the day, to their cosy firesides in the distant suburbs. They leave the city to those who can afford to patronise the theatres, restaurants and bars, and to those unfortunates who can afford none of these oases that can make a wintry London bearable.

4

I came out of the memory as the bus laboured around the corner from Haymarket into Trafalgar Square. I gazed out upon the throng of placard-bearing demonstrators keeping up their round-the-clock vigil outside South Africa House, directly across the square. Placards raised, the protestors paced up and down in front of the embassy, chanting, demanding Nelson Mandela's release from prison. Not for the first time, I wondered why I'd never seen a black or even a brown face amid the protestors.

My groggy mind fled back to the article on London. It dimly occurred to me that I was one of those unfortunates it had referred to; an unfortunate who had just completed a wearisome eight-hour stint on the 'graveyard shift'; an unfortunate who had just boarded the bus outside his workplace – the fast-food emporium of McDonald's. Perhaps all the blacks in London were unfortunates. Perhaps we all slaved away those ungodly hours at McDonald's, and could find neither the time nor the strength to join the fight against de Klerk's oppressive apartheid regime.

My gloved hands, aching with cold, were buried deep in my jacket pocket. I leaned forward slightly, shoulders hunched, and glanced across at my blurred reflection in the side window pane. I wondered what racial tag the people of London would ascribe to me. With my light complexion, perhaps some might deem me Mediterranean or Middle Eastern. But my overgrown, coarse hair

5

which, according to my Chinese classmates, resembled a black motorcycle helmet, told a different story. It spoke of my African roots. Yet my oriental eye-folds and brown almond-shaped eyes might indicate to many that I carried, somewhere in my veins, a trace of oriental blood.

Could I be the product of some long-held family secret?

A wry smile tugged at my lips as I called to mind my one-time school nickname, *'No-race'*. It hadn't seemed quite so funny back then.

From the upper deck I took in the low-flying-bird's-eye view as the bus wended its way along the busy streets of the metropolis. I squinted out at the enormous structures of steel, concrete, and glass, marching by outside the window. Heavy traffic chugged by – vehicles of every make, shape, size, and description, but none so numerous as the big, red double-decker buses and those glistening black cabs resembling giant beetles.

Stifling a yawn with the back of my hand, I caught a glimpse of the advertising panel of the bus that revved past. The British Airways advertisement urged Londoners: *Fly BA – your Favourite Airline*. This took my mind right back to the hazardous eight-hour flight across the Atlantic from St. Lucia, two months before; an unnerving experience for a first-time traveller. Landing on British soil, though, was, for me, nothing short of a dream – a childhood fantasy come true; one of many steps along the long, arduous road towards fulfilling my life's goal.

But the last two months had been one disaster after another. That long road now seemed a steep and slippery slope. Too many disappointments. Too many dashed hopes. Doubt now consumed me like a cancer.

I closed my eyes and drew a long, harsh breath, searching the empty reservoir of my spirit for a scrap of motivation. *I must move on*, I told myself. But my gloom persisted. A dull ache pounded in my head as I stared straight ahead at nothing, scenes from the past few years tumbling through my mind. I wondered where I'd be today had it not been for the private institution that had redeemed me, giving me one final opportunity to pursue secondary education after twice failing the common entrance exams. It was at the Seventh Day Adventist Academy that I'd set my sights on my chosen profession. Accountancy.

Bookkeeping had come a long way since Bob Cratchit had sat on his high stool in Scrooge's counting house. Now, all of industry needed "bean counters". It seemed that more and more leaders of industry hailed from the ranks of that profession. I had found my path; a means of escape from an otherwise doomed future.

The two-thousand-pound loan I'd scrounged off the St. Lucia Development Bank would barely meet the cost of a full year's tuition. If only the bank would pay the money over to me, I'd be able to juggle a little and make ends meet, somehow. But rules were rules. The fees would be paid directly to the college. All the same, I took my sparse savings, my hopes and aspirations, and headed for London and the private college in Greenwich, in the south east of the great city.

Now, as I sat shivering in my front row seat of Bus Number Twelve, terrible doubts assailed me. My mind wandered off to that moment, not so long ago, when I'd faced imminent disaster.

That dismally cold Saturday evening three weeks before, desperate to hear a friendly, familiar voice, I had left the confines of my frigid room and, braving the bitter cold, trudged up the misty road to the nearest public payphone that stood next to a heavily graffitied wall.

I recalled only too well the phone booth: a fully enclosed structure of red-painted steel and glass, which had a special kind of odour – a mingling of stale beer, tobacco, and more than a hint of urine. Perhaps to take the user's mind off the aroma, the local ladies of the night had stuck their business cards and graphic posters haphazardly over the insides of the glass panels.

Inhaling lightly, my eyes scanned the explicit poster of a self-proclaimed 'blonde bombshell' down on all fours. I pressed the phone to my ear, and dialled the eleven digits that would connect me to my friend in St. Lucia. I heard the ring tone four thousand miles across the Atlantic, and could almost feel the warm breezes flowing off the coastal waters of the Caribbean Sea.

But the sing-song voice that answered wasn't that of my closest friend.

"No, man, sorry, Ivan gone to the beach for the day."

Those words sent my heart plummeting down into the depths of despair, taking my spirit with it. Almost too much to bear – so unfair, I'd thought. *The beach for the day! While I freeze my butt in this huge fridge. Never again shall I complain of the Caribbean heat or even a hurricane or two.*

Visions of my friends kicking a football up and down the warm, golden sands of Reduit beach, under the blazing sun and blue skies pranced about in my head as I left the phone box and the temporary shelter it gave from the chilly wind that blew down the grey and unfriendly street outside. I trudged back stiffly in the bitter cold to the charmless surroundings of my room, where I took an inventory. My worldly wealth consisted of two eggs, a loaf of bread and a solitary five-pound note.

Then I dug into my pockets . . .

What? Wait a minute! Where's the five-pound note? My last five pounds!

An agonised search of my room failed to find it. A frantic retrace of my steps to the telephone booth turned up nothing. My last five pounds had gone. Disappeared. Lost.

My face puffed with despair, quivering chin propped upon my gloved fist, I'd sat at the wooden table in the crispy cold basement kitchen, and surveyed my reduced wealth laid out in front of me.

Two eggs and a loaf of bread. Something had to be done.

With an awful, wrenching pain, I felt I had little option but to sell my one valuable possession; my gold bracelet, which had been a going-away gift from my aunt. A tough decision, for the bracelet had tremendous sentimental value. In its former incarnation as a substantial band of gold it had graced the wedding finger of my late grandmother for over forty years. My Aunt Sheila had had the ring reformed into a glistening, slender bracelet, with 'Rudy' emblazoned on its nameplate.

I'd swallowed my pride and shame, and with my heart galloping in my chest, trod reluctantly over to the small jewellers shops along Lewisham High Street, trying to sell my bracelet. One after the other, the jewellers' faces twisted with cynicism, their eyes narrowing to slits of suspicion. They refused to have anything to do with me. I imagined what was going through their minds – *An ethnic man, even a pale-complexioned one, trying to hock a gold bracelet? Had to be hot. So it has his name engraved on it? So what? No thanks!*

No luck in Lewisham, I rode the Number Thirty-Six bus the ten minutes or so to Peckham High Street, where a squat, large-bellied, gold-toothed, pale-skinned man with hair in a messy jet-black pony-tail, grey showing at the roots, haggled with me over price. When I vehemently refused to accept a mere twenty pounds to part with the bracelet, he threatened to set the police on me. Anger flooded his steely blue eyes, as, in his barely decipherable Cockney accent, he roared in my face: "You thieving bastard! I'll call the bobbies on you . . . put you behind bars . . . I will!"

The sudden onrush of hostility had shot a bolt of fear through me. I'd rushed off in stunned embarrassment, controlling my desire to break into a run, feeling the glare of onlookers boring into my retreating back. The barrage of obscenities the man hurled in my face and at my back lingered for some time, eventually finding its way into my dreams.

Since then, that nightmare – running from the police, cornered – had haunted me.

But that was two weeks ago. Now, lounging in the front seats on the top deck, my flesh prickled with shame as I cringed at the memory. I felt only slightly consoled when I glanced down at the 'reddish-gold' bracelet on my left wrist. I reached across and turned-over the nameplate, smiling ruefully at the dark spot where the belligerent jeweller's harsh chemical had stained the surface, proving the metal to be genuine Guyanese gold.

It would take considerably more than twenty pounds to entice me to part with my late grandmother's wedding ring.

Again my thoughts wheeled back. After I'd gone two days without so much as a bite of stale bread, with a groaning stomach and lacerated pride, I had put a call through to my Aunt Toya in Manchester, seeking a loan. The fifty pounds – not a loan, but a grant, my aunt insisted – had arrived in the mail the next day, and had kept me going a full week.

But the McDonald's job had been the final solution to my dire money woes. I worked the graveyard shift from eleven at night till seven next morning before heading off to college. Cleaning, scrubbing, stacking, preparing for the morning rush; the job was an endless chore. But it wasn't long before the initial euphoria of having solved a financial crisis rapidly dissipated, once it dawned upon me that the job produced a lifestyle that shut out anything in the way of finding time to sleep.

Hence, this chilly February morning, after seven straight nights on the graveyard shift, I felt like a used battery: spent, drained. Physically and mentally.

Slouched sideways in my seat, I glanced across to my left, at the only other occupant of the top deck. The old man, with dishevelled blond hair and a heavy sagging face filigreed with tiny red blood vessels near the surface of his cheeks, had been snoring loudly for several long minutes. Only seconds ago he had awakened with a strangled snort. A tattered plaid blanket draping his shoulders, he leaned back in his seat, his bloodshot eyes staring straight ahead, seemingly at something that wasn't there. The stench of stale alcohol emanating from his body drifted over to me, sending a wave of nausea sweeping through my souring stomach.

An uncanny sense of foreboding overwhelmed me, forcing my mind to one of my co-workers at

McDonald's. Robert, a short, bow-legged black man in his mid-thirties but looking fifty-something, was a sad figure from Ghana who had come to England fifteen years before, to pursue, like me, an accountancy qualification. Now, half way through life's contract, he seemed a permanent, sulking fixture on the graveyard shift.

The questions tormenting my mind were: *Could this happen to me? Could I end up like this?*

A piercing ping! penetrated my churning thoughts, and they evaporated. A passenger on the bottom deck had pressed the red button signalling the driver to stop. The bus screeched to a halt, sending my head clashing painfully against the cold reinforced glass panel.

I was still grimacing a minute or so later when I turned and saw a late-middle-aged woman with stringy grey hair and a long dark overcoat struggling to pull her ample body up the spiral metal stairs at the back of the bus. Two infant boys in smart blue blazers and grey shorts had clambered aboard ahead of the woman. I smiled at the fresh-faced blue-eyed boys, but turned away quickly when the woman frowned disapproval at me as she hustled them down the aisle, taking seats several rows away from me, closer to the seemingly homeless drunk.

My head throbbed in tune with the labouring engine as I returned my gaze to the cold grey streets outside. Dark-skinned men in fingerless gloves and neon jackets bent to pick up litter along the pavements; traffic wardens stalked their prey; delivery drivers manoeuvred their trucks behind lamp-posts; hawkers stood in front of kiosks, waving newspapers along pavements teeming with besuited people buzzing about in every direction.

The bus slowed in heavy traffic, and inched past Embankment underground station. I spotted a figure lying on the cold pavement next to the entrance. He seemed lost in slumber, curled up in the foetal position, loose cardboard sheets partly covering his body that seemed clothed in nothing but soiled rags. His pale face was littered with black blotches. A large, black furry dog nestled besides him. The pair seemed oblivious of the crowd rushing up and down on the pavement alongside them.

I shook my head, slowly, incredulously, for I'd never thought such a sight would greet me in the mother country. It occurred to me just how misinformed I'd been over the years. Perhaps the Brits were mere mortals after all.

A minute or so passed. The bus was squeaking to a halt behind a garbage truck. I watched as the men in fingerless gloves and neon jackets hurried to unload dustbins into the back of the truck. All the men were ethnic, of African descent, black. West Indian?

Had they too arrived with hopes and dreams? Why did they find it so difficult to acquire an education and to progress?

British nationals had a vast array of opportunities before them . . . help through educational grants of every kind, shape, and form. *But what of these*?

A raspy male voice with a vaguely familiar accent, roused me back to the present: "Tickets please. Tickets please."

I craned my neck. Looming over me was a lanky, middle-aged black man with thinning grey hair and a face that was drawn, pinched. His dark grey suit hung loosely from his wiry body, a ticket machine suspended from the worn leather strap around his neck.

He glared down at me. "You deaf?"

I tried to place the accent. *Jamaican?*

Clumsy with cold, my gloved fingers fumbled frantically in my jacket pocket for my bus fare. The conductor squinted his deep-set, tired eyes at me, shaking his head ruefully, as though I were the bane of his existence.

I quickly counted the coins my fingers had found, and passed thirty-five pence to the conductor.

He cranked the machine. A narrow strip of flimsy paper came speeding out of the slit in the base. He tore off the ticket and flung it at me. Incredulous, I watched it float down to the floor at my feet.

With undisguised indignation, my eyes followed the man as he turned and trudged unsteadily down the aisle, toward the back of the bus and down the spiral metal stairs, clasping, with some effort, the chrome railings, to support his weight.

I soon found myself wondering what his dreams had been when first he had set foot on British soil.

15

That strange foreboding again. *Could this happen to me?*

Gazing out upon the imperial splendours of London, I shook my head vigorously, trying to clear my mind. The bus trundled past the Houses of Parliament with their Gothic architecture, groaned past the imposing tower housing Big Ben, then revved across Westminster Bridge, over the dark, grey waters of the Thames. County Hall slowly receded into the background. As if deciding it had provided enough touristy entertainment for one day, the Number Twelve headed towards the less picturesque South East London.

Outside, the sky was cold and grey, rain now sheeting itself against the window, deepening my gloom.

I reached into my haversack for my well-thumbed copy of Norman Vincent Peale's *The Power of Positive Thinking*, my constant companion. But I was just too beat even to read a chapter or two to get a little inspiration. I simply caressed the tattered paperback with a gloved hand as I leaned back in my seat, my eyes closing, opening, closing . . .

Twenty head-drooping minutes later, having changed buses on Peckham High Street in front of Kisses Night Club, the Number Thirty-Six deposited me along Lewisham Way, a good five-minute walk to my bed-sit.

Under cold grey skies, people were rushing about here and there, heavy overcoats flapping behind them, collars turned up against the wind. A thin

16

layer of frost covered the ground. I could feel the cold rising through the soles of my sneakers, numbing my feet. I turned left into Elswick Road, a crescent-shaped, stolidly Victorian development of bay-windowed terraced houses. Against bitterly cold winds billowing down the mist-filled street, I trudged along stiffly to number 219, feeling the chill penetrating my beige corduroys, the icy air rushing through my jacket.

A shiver rippled through me as I gave myself a hard mental shake. *I can't afford to fail – there is too much at stake.*

Moments later, I fumbled my key into the door lock, and no sooner had I slammed the door behind me than I was making my way briskly along the narrow corridor that wasn't much warmer than outside. My key opened the door at the end of the corridor, and I entered my cold, darkened room.

I flicked the wall switch. The single light bulb, suspended from the centre of the ceiling, lit up the medium-sized room.

My drooping eyes surveyed my domain. Everything seemed in place: the small book-laden table with its wooden chair in front of it; the comfortably shabby armchair in the corner; the monstrously tall and top-heavy wardrobe that teetered unsteadily on its too-small base; the little red clock on the little bedside table; the short and narrow bed upon which my landlord's eight-year-old daughter had once slept.

I didn't need to touch the central heating panel

in the far corner of the room, to know that it hadn't the slightest hint of warmth. It wasn't that my Barbadian landlord was stingy. The man simply felt he had to exercise due fiscal prudence in respect of a tenant who contributed only twenty pounds weekly towards the cost of running the household.

As I did, ritually, upon entering my room, I let my eyes climb the left lateral wall to the thumb-tacked scribbled quotation of an anonymous poet.

> *The heights that great men reach and kept*
> *Were not attained by sudden flight,*
> *But they, whilst their companions slept,*
> *Were toiling onwards through the night.*

Perhaps I had taken the words literally, for I was always toiling, never resting. The closeness of the south eastern railway that ran outside my window with annoying regularity severely jeopardized what little chance of rest I had. Sometimes in the middle of my fitful sleep, it seemed the boisterous locomotives ran right through my room.

Unnerving sounds from the railway or not, I just had to grab a few minutes' sleep. Shivering from the chill that seeped through the walls of the house, making it frigid and damp, I collapsed heavily, fully clothed – sneakers and all – onto the short and narrow wooden bed.

I flicked a glance at the little red clock on my bedside table. Seven forty-five. Not much time. By quarter past eight, I was expected at my desk in room 102 at my college in Greenwich, a ten-minute bus ride away.

A fifteen-minute snooze should do the trick . . . recharge my batteries. I coiled up like a little child in bed sucking its thumb.

CHAPTER 2

The deafening clamour of the boisterous trains rushing along the rail tracks outside my window penetrated my short, fitful sleep. My eyes refused to stay open or closed.

I tried to calm myself, my nerves. But no sooner did I feel my body begin to relax than I heard the distant roar of yet another oncoming train, a roar that grew louder and louder with each passing second until the explosive rumble blasted through my room, rattling my wardrobe, chair, table and bed, reverberating through the walls, through the entire brick structure.

The thunderous roar tormented my soul, seeming like a never-ending earthquake.

It felt like a lifetime before the interminable noise faded off into the distance, the rattling waned, and the room fell once more into a tomblike silence around me.

Stretched out now on my narrow bed that was

shorter than I was long, I willed my mind, my muscles, my body, to relax. *Relax . . .*

I must have dozed, for I felt my heavy eyelids fluttering open again. Something had woken me. Then I thought I heard not the usual annoying rumble of passing trains, but a distant, faintly recognisable, melody. What's more, it seemed to be playing right outside my bedroom door.

Mary had a Little Lamb kept chiming over and over again, louder and louder.

I knew I'd heard that annoying tune somewhere, but where? I searched my groggy mind.

Then I found it.

My landlord had replaced the robust cast-iron knocker with an electronic battery-powered device that chimed the nursery rhyme to announce a visitor at the door. In my groggy confusion, the staccato chimes resonated bitterly around the room, and in my head.

In sudden surprised bewilderment, I flipped over onto my left side, and shot a glance at the little red clock on my bed-side table.

Nine fifteen.

Damn! I'm late for college! I overslept!

I bolted upright, and leapt off the bed, feeling a rush of blood to my head as I made a dash for the door. I leaped over the haversack left in the middle of the floor, but landed on rubbery legs that instantly gave way beneath me, the impetus catapulting me forward, sending my arms flailing wildly about me. My head seemed to explode against the doorknob.

Collapsed to my knees, my mind momentarily blanked, I saw a kaleidoscope of stars twinkling before my eyes. I willed the room to stop spinning, but round and round it went, and on and on the door kept chiming. Then the room slowed to a reluctant stop, the twinkling stars fizzling into oblivion.

But *Mary had a Little Lamb* kept on chiming.

At that instant my one goal in life was to reach the front door.

I shook my head vigorously to clear the lingering dizziness, and hoisted myself unsteadily up from the floor.

Searing pain was slicing through my head as I found myself swaying down the narrow corridor, heading for the persistent front door.

I turned the doorknob and pulled it. A blinding flash of white light hit me like a laser in my eyes. I reeled under the scalding pain and flung my hands up to cover my eyes. Just then a gush of icy air lashed my face. Dazed, I stood in the doorway as another sudden bolt of pain shot through my forehead, then another, and another.

From somewhere I heard a vague disembodied female voice chirp, "Good morning, Sir. I was wondering if . . ."

But all I saw before my eyes were flickering spots of bright light against a velvety blackness.

"Sir?"

I blinked and squinted hard, then rubbed my

eyes vigorously. When I opened them, it was the same velvety blackness that greeted me. My pulse began to sprint.

"Sir."

I was rubbing my eyes again, then blinking and squinting. The darkness persisted. My heart jolted violently and I felt an awful sinking sensation in my gut as if I'd missed a step going downstairs.

Then I heard myself shouting, "I can't see, I can't see!"

"Can I help you sir?"

"I can't see, I can't see!"

"Sir, are you okay?"

"Sorry . . . I can't see you . . . I have to go!"

I slammed the door shut, rattling the wooden frame.

Heart pounding wildly in my chest, head throbbing, nerves simmering, I felt a nameless terror. I stretched my hands out in front of me, and turned around in the suffocating blackness, trying to picture the passageway. I followed the wall with my hands, careering back down the corridor, my eyes blinking incessantly, but seeing nothing . . . nothing but the heart-wrenching blackness.

When I reached the end of the passageway, I groped for my bedroom door. I gritted my teeth against the scorching pain in my forehead as I entered the room gingerly and felt my way across the floor to my bed. I lay myself down slowly, cautiously, feeling spasms of pain searing through my head, like surges of electricity.

23

Still my eyes saw nothing – nothing but blackness. Perhaps if I were to shut them for a few quiet moments all would be well?

I clenched my eyes shut. When I slid them open, seconds later, still nothing. My heart sank.

Again, I shut my eyes. Opened them.

Nothing. Nothing. Nothing.

Nothing but that awful velvety blackness.

I felt panic overwhelming me, my head screaming in anguish, incoherent frightful thoughts tumbling around in my head. Despite the frigidity of my room, sweat now dampened my body.

I decided I could do nothing but lie there in my agony, and rest . . . rest my aching head, my sightless eyes.

It will be okay, I just need to relax a little. Relax. Relax. Relax.

Again, I shut my eyes, this time more gently. I inhaled slowly, deeply, then gradually exhaled; over and over again, I followed that routine. After what seemed like two minutes later, heart thumping, I eased my eyes open.

Nothing. Not a glimmer of light, not a ray of hope. My heart was now threatening to burst out my chest.

I coiled into the foetal position again, folded my arms tightly across my chest, and lay there, listening to the pounding of my heart and head, tasting despair like salt in my mouth.

CHAPTER 3

Head throbbing, heart pounding, I pinched my inner left arm hoping to awaken from this hellish nightmare that had brought my dreams, hopes, and aspirations to an abrupt, devastating end, four thousand miles from home.

Nothing happened . . . just the stinging pain in my arm.

Then my fingers began rubbing vigorously at my itching eyes.

Then I opened them.

Still nothing . . . nothing but velvety blackness.

Come on Rudy. Come on man! Come on!

I blinked. I blinked again. And again.

Nothing. Nothing. Nothing.

Blackness engulfed my world. It was over. I was finished. Done.

What will become of me now? What on earth should I do? Over and over again, these dismal thoughts resonated in my head.

But my brain supplied no answers.

Outside my window, I heard the approaching distant rumble of yet another hurrying train. Then with each passing second, the clatter grew louder and louder as the iron tracks sparked, buckled and grinded under the weight and speed of the train, until the explosive clamour, heightened by the blasting of the horn, erupted relentlessly through my room. I lay there on my small bed, feeling the vibration reverberate through my body, engulfing me, tormenting my very soul. My chaotic mind pleaded for the locomotive to complete its thunderous passage as I felt my blood pressure rising and rising. With every strenuous throb of blood through my arteries, the pounding between my eyes intensified, pulsating in tune with my thumping heart.

Then gradually, mercifully, I heard the deafening rumble fading away, fading into the distance . . . until it was no more.

Though the room eventually settled into silence around me, my nerves continued to simmer with dread.

And as the lives of drowning men are said to flash before their eyes, memories of my past kept flickering in my suffocating darkness.

My mind transported me back to another place, another time, long, long, long ago:

> *No mummy's kisses . . .*
> *No daddy's smiles . . .*
> *Nobody wants me – I'm nobody's child.*

I knelt on the wooden chair in front of the window, my small chin propped upon my fists, elbows digging into the window-sill, absently humming my favourite song playing on the radiogram in the sunny drawing room behind me.

From the upper window of the old semi-wooden house in LaClery – a community in Castries, the capital of St. Lucia, I gazed out upon the sun-softened asphalt road, a whiff of its tarry odour drifting up to me. My eyes were fixed expectantly upon the distant corner near the inter-section with Lance Road.

I had just turned five. Or was it six?

Donned in my favourite plaid short-sleeves over brown crimplene shorts, I wiggled my bare feet excitedly off the back of the chair as I awaited the crowning moment of my day. Every day, like this, I awaited my aunt's return from work . . . this was my afternoon vigil, awaiting my Aunt Sheila.

In the sunny room behind me, my sister sat on the linoleum floor, playing with her little blonde doll, absorbed in her own little fantasy world.

For me, life in the household wasn't a bed of roses. Apart from my Grenadian grandmother – known to all as 'Mother' – my Aunt Sheila was my only shield from the wanton teasing of the others at home – a mixture of aunts, uncles, cousins, and others. For my sister, Roslyn, busy dressing and grooming her doll, things didn't seem quite as tough. But with my very light, almost white complexion, and vaguely oriental and slightly

27

girlish looks, I seemed always the butt of ridicule
. . . ridicule that sometimes came from beyond our
household.

Either that or I was just too sensitive a little boy.

Now, as every day, eagerly I awaited Sheila's
return home from work. Each day she would bring
us some little treat. Perhaps today it would be
sponge cake or ice cream, or maybe coconut balls
or fudge. My mouth began to water. I prayed it
would be coconut balls today – yellow, green, pink,
orange, white, coconut balls. I licked my lips in
greedy anticipation.

It wasn't that I was terribly hungry, though. Not
half an hour ago I had devoured a bowl of milky jelly
from the bunch of coconuts Albert had picked from
the tall, thin tree that stood on the river bank towards
the back of the house. But I wouldn't have a problem
finding space in my stomach for the delicacies Sheila
bought from the roadside vendors as she strolled the
mile or so up from downtown Castries.

I gazed out past the spidery branches of the tall
avocado tree, seeing a cross-section of life going by
along the street below. Motor vehicles of all makes,
shapes, sizes, ages, and colours drove by. My grandmother once told me that my blind grandfather –
a man everyone called Chung Li – had once owned
a car. A man named Oscar chauffeured him around.

One day I'll own a brand-new Zephyr, I told myself,
my eyes riveted on the distant corner as I absently
hummed the song about mummy's kisses and
daddy's smiles.

I marvelled at the colourfully painted buses that frequently trundled by beneath my window, labouring under the weight of their crowded passengers and the sacks of vegetables, fruits, charcoal, and other items stacked on their wooden rooftops.

A more sombre sight, that I hoped not to witness today, was the sorrowful processions that passed frequently beneath my window. A slow-moving hearse, laden with colourful wreaths and blaring out a mournful dirge would be followed on foot by a company of mourners. Wearing grim, stricken faces, amid copious weeping and wailing, they followed the dead to their resting place in the cemetery on the beach.

Sometimes there was no hearse at all. In the scorching heat, two rows of sweating, panting men making quick uneven strides, clasping the ends of planks on which the coffin was set, would lead the mournful procession to the cemetery.

I wondered if that was how it had been for my blind grandfather, who had hailed from the tiny island of Bequia, in St. Vincent and the Grenadines.

At times I would spot a lone figure dressed in black and white, hands down at his sides, a child-sized coffin balanced on his padded head as he marched along briskly to the cemetery. Oftentimes, I wondered about the tiny body stretched out in the coffin. Why was the man alone? Where were the mourners? How old was the child? Where were its parents?

I leaned farther out the window to my left. Beyond the ravine, I could see the dense woods of the Devaux family's estate. The wealthy white family were owners of M&C, Sheila's employer.

Local legend had it that 'boloms' – mysterious evil spirits inhabiting the bodies of children – haunted the woods bordering my home. 'Boloms' were originally an African legend, I later learned, brought to the Caribbean by the slaves who, over the years, had kept the myth alive. For most St. Lucians, though, the legend had more immediacy, and even the most sceptical had a sneaky suspicion that the creatures really did exist. As no one had actually seen one, their horrid descriptions and mischievous deeds depended largely upon the lively imagination of children . . . children like me.

Now, at long last, in the distance, I spied Sheila as she rounded the corner. Slim and poised in her uniform, she carried herself with an air of elegance, seemingly in defiance of her surroundings. She betrayed no signs of bearing the weight of feeding an entire compound family on her cashier's salary that was not much more than one hundred US dollars monthly.

A warm rush of joy and comfort consumed me as I knelt on my chair in front of my window. Now I felt safe, secure. No one dared mess with me now. No one dared call me *Bètje Pouvre*. I hated being called 'a poor white man' in Creole, the local dialect more popularly spoken than English.

Like a happy little pup making happy little barks

and wagging its happy little tail, I waggled my feet off the back of the chair, shouting, "Aunty Sheila, Aunty Sheila!"

Hearing my excitement, Roslyn scrambled to her feet, and bolted to the window, bumping me off my chair. A moment later, she was dashing across the drawing room, her footfalls making splattering sounds against the creaky wooden linoleum floor.

I quickly hoisted myself off the floor, hurriedly brushed off my shorts, and bolted across the living room, plummeting down the creaky staircase, into the dining room and out the front door.

"Aunty Sheila! Aunty Sheila!" We shouted in unison, stopping abruptly before our aunt as she descended the concrete steps that led down from the roadside. Our faces wreathed in overbright smiles, our eyes danced in merriment.

Sheila's kindly, smiling brown face greeted us. She seemed just as overjoyed to see us as we were to see her.

More than once, I'd heard our aunt and grandmother joking among themselves, that it was only when we spotted our aunt coming down the hill, did we ever call her 'Aunty Sheila' . . . usually, it would be simply 'Sheila'. Perhaps they were right. We weren't used to calling anyone by any name other than their first name. I didn't know why. No matter. That's just the way it was. But seeing our aunt at the end of the day . . . well . . . that was something else.

The pleasant smile lingered on her full lips as

she made her way through the wooden door that had never known paint. We followed anxiously, nudging each other in the ribs, giggling, our eyes glistening in anticipation, and riveted on her handbag.

Then Sheila uttered the question we had anxiously awaited. "Guess what I brought you today?"

"Coconut balls!"

"Ice cream!"

Smiling happily, she stood in front of the dining table, and fished a little clear plastic bag from her handbag.

When my eyes spotted the colourful coconut balls, my heart began leaping with joy. No sooner had Roslyn and I began to jump all over the place than we started to stuff our mouths, munching away with rabid delight.

Then two neighbourhood boys around my age, clad only in underwear, bolted through the front door and halted abruptly in front of us. We ignored the pair who stood right there before us, smiling in anticipation, licking their lips as the sweetness exploded in my mouth, shooting down my throat.

Sheila's voice rang through from the kitchen, scolding us for being too greedy.

I nudged Roslyn, who broke half a ball in two and shared her bounty. Mine was all gone, and I wanted more.

Two days later, Sunday, Roslyn and I glowed with

excitement as we grasped Sheila's hands. We were strolling up the hill, on our way to George the Fifth Park, known to most as the Gardens.

I urged that we should cross the road long before we reached the Devaux lane at the intersection of Calvary Road and the steep Darling Road. There was no telling what we might encounter as we moved in closer to the private lane that disappeared uphill into the darkened woods – it could easily be one of those boloms waiting to pounce.

We looked left, then right, and swiftly crossed the road. Fifteen minutes later we were making our way into the Gardens. We strolled along footpaths that were ablaze with colour – a sea of red, orange, yellow, and pink blossoms. The day was warm, but a constant sea breeze kept the sun from venting its full fury upon the land. Up above, fluffy white clouds floated idly in the blue expanse of sky. The aroma of roasting peanuts and cashew nuts drifted through the air. Passers-by dressed in their Sunday best greeted each other with bright smiles and a cheerful 'Good afternoon'. We smiled at children ambling along with mothers or fathers or both, as we possessively clung to our aunt.

After Sheila had pushed us to and fro on the swings, we sat on the green wooden bench in the shade of a palm tree laden with bunches of the bright orange fruit.

I asked our aunt the question that I'd asked time and again: "Sheila, where is our mother and our father?"

The pictures adorning our living room wall provided the only evidence of our parents' existence – Rosemary, squatting in a queenly fashion in a knitted sleeveless dress, a beautiful gold necklace around her neck, smiled down upon us, her narrow heavy-lidded eyes seeming to follow our every movement around the room. And, in a smaller black-and-white photograph, Rodney, half-smiling, stood tall and slender next to a single bed. His long-sleeved shirt, casually open at the throat, was tucked into his shiny tight trousers.

Sheila's expression took on a faraway look, as it always did whenever that question arose.

She hesitated a moment, as if coming to an important decision. Then with a gentle solemn voice, said, "Your father, Rodney, is in England making lots of money for you all. And your mother, Rosemary, is there too. Very soon they will be sending for you all."

"But when?" Roslyn asked, her voice pleading, another question our aunt had come to expect.

Sheila smiled, wistfully. "Oh, soon. You have to be patient. These things take time, child."

Then we listened open-mouthed, smiling occasionally, as our mother's older sister told us, not for the first time, about our parents.

Roslyn's face spread into a broad grin when Sheila mentioned that Roslyn had been born in Barbados. My sister asked if I was jealous. I lied and said no.

Sheila explained that her family had once lived

in Barbados for very many years. Rodney, our father, a Barbadian, had lived a few doors down from the family. He and my mother had been together since their early teens. Rodney was eighteen when Roslyn was born; our mother had just turned sixteen. When my mother's family relocated to St. Lucia, Rodney followed some months after. I was born a year later. But that was after a frustrated Rodney, unable to find work in St. Lucia, had left for England. Our mother followed within the year.

My sister and I were still waiting to join our parents.

We lived only for that day.

CHAPTER 4

The mid-morning sun was flaming from above, streaming into the living room from which Bing Cosby was crooning his 'White Christmas' on the radiogram.

For a change, Roslyn wasn't grooming her doll. She had joined me kneeling on my wooden chair in front of the window, gazing out upon the street below.

"Look at these boys!" Roslyn's voice said suddenly, humorously.

I jerked my wandering attention from the fluffy cloud formation in the bright blue sky, my gaze darting up and down the road: "Where? Where?"

Then I spotted them.

The two bare-topped boys in tattered shorts were sprinting down the sun-softened asphalt road, heading for town, their bare feet slapping the road. Sweat dripping from their glistening dark bodies, fear in their eyes, they kept shooting terrified glances over their shoulders as if trying desperately to outrun some nameless monster hot in pursuit.

My curiosity turned to excitement, then fear, then panic. This could only mean one thing.

Roslyn, older and sharper than me, got it first. "Cows! Cows! Cows!" she shouted, "Rudy . . . cows!"

I jerked a terrified glance down to my red jersey, a bolt of dread shooting right through me.

"Hurry!" Roslyn screamed, nudging me off the chair.

A frantic second later, I was scurrying across the drawing room floor, peeling off my red jersey, just one thought on my mind as I bolted for the bedroom. Not ten seconds later, heart still thumping hard and fast, I scurried back to the window, taking to my shaky knees on the chair next to my relieved seven-year-old sister.

My red jersey had given way to a light blue tee-shirt. Mercifully, I'd averted a horrid fate. *Thank God!* I quickly made the sign of the cross.

My gaze flew to the stumpy old man lashing his long whip, pulling with all his might on the taut rope noosed around the neck of long-horned, bellowing bull, forcing it around the corner from Raymond's little grocery shop. My heart began to flutter again. I cast another petrified glance at my tee-shirt, just to confirm one last time that it was not in fact, red.

Blue . . . good.

The stumpy, brown-skinned man was dripping

with sweat. His tattered shirt was unbuttoned and fell over the ragged trousers tucked into knee-high black rubber boots. He kept lashing and pulling the rebellious bull, trying to steer it towards town.

I heaved a huge sigh of relief after beast and master tussled past my window without incident.

"You lucky, boy," Roslyn breathed, relieved.

"Yeah, I know" I said, crossing myself quickly, my lips moving in silent prayer, for I knew that had the bull spotted my red jersey all hell would have broken loose. Instantly, it would have been reminded of blood, whereupon it would glimpse the violent fate to which it was being led at the Castries abattoir. That would have driven the animal stark raving mad, hunting down and killing whoever wore the red that had foretold its slaughter. It preferred to remain blissfully unaware of its fate. It wouldn't have mattered that I had been sitting on the top floor of the house; the deranged bull would have leaped up through the window, tearing me to shreds, as the older boys had warned Roslyn and me.

I heaved a huge sigh, happy and relieved to have averted such a terrible disaster.

My lips again moved in silent prayer as I watched the bull disappear reluctantly up the hill. And I found myself wondering about the two boys who were running ahead, and whether they, too, had quickly peeled off red jerseys and thrown them away. Just then, a big bus painted in the colours of the rainbow skidded to a halt on the side of the recently-paved road, crunching gravel, sending a thick cloud of grey dust billowing up.

From within the bus, I heard uproarious laughter amid loud, babbling Creole voices.

My eyes followed a fat, light-skinned woman with long glistening black hair, her round face slicked with sweat, as she squeezed and panted her way down from the back of the bus. From beneath the back rows of the planks on which the passengers sat, she pulled out a freshly cut Christmas tree. She lifted it onto her head with apparent ease, then, without looking down, stooped and picked up two large plastic bags fairly bursting with green bananas, yams, dasheens.

Just then, gasping for breath, a chubby light-skinned boy, clad in tight brown shorts and a yellow tee-shirt bearing a picture of Daffy Duck on the front, jumped out from the back of the idling bus, as if he'd been left behind. He reached out a chubby hand and grabbed the woman's flared skirt as she marched briskly toward Agard Hill, balancing the Christmas tree on her padded head, both her hands stretched down at her sides, clasping the overburdened plastic bags. The boy straggled behind, with short, uneven strides. His attention seemed focused entirely on licking the big red lollipop clasped in his other hand.

With my elbows digging into the grooved window-sill, cheeks resting between my palms, I barely moved my head as my eyes tracked the little boy who seemed no older than me.

As if he'd sensed my gaze, he turned around abruptly and flicked a large red tongue out at me, as if to say, 'Your mouth could lick . . . you're getting none!"

The fat woman beckoned him to hurry up. He quickened his pace, returning his attention to his lollipop.

My mouth was already watering.

"I'm hungry" I whispered to Roslyn, who knelt quietly on the chair beside me, her thick-lidded, almond-shaped eyes following a dark-skinned man whose enormous belly, stretched out beyond his unbuttoned white shirt, revealed a navel no smaller than a tennis ball. He trudged briskly but unsteadily up the hill that led past the McNamara mansion, clasping two clear plastic bags filled with green, yellow, white, orange icicles.

Hunger began to pester me.

"I feel like eating something," I whispered again, shifting my gaze back to the little boy and the woman just as they were about to turn the corner that led up the dusty footpath to Agard Hill.

"Me too. Let's go and look for something to eat," Roslyn whispered back.

She jumped off the chair, and bolted across the floor, plummeting down the stairs. I thundered after her, trying to leap down the stairs, two at a time, unsuccessfully.

After rummaging through the kitchen cupboards and the fridge, without success, we scampered back upstairs, heading for the bedrooms.

Five belly-groaning minutes later, I spotted, tucked away behind a pile of magazines atop the tall wardrobe in Sheila's room, a tube-like plastic bottle stuffed with mouth-watering tiny yellow sweets. I grabbed the little bottle and slid down onto the old sewing machine, stepped onto the red leatherette seat of the wrought-iron stool, and jumped down to the floor with a thump.

"Sweets! Sweets! Sweets!" I shouted, waving the bottle, as I scampered for the drawing room.

Roslyn came tearing into the room, almost bumping into me as I stood there struggling to open the tightly shut bottle that had a white label bearing tiny letters I couldn't read.

She snatched the bottle from my hand. One hard twist later, and little yellow sweets spilled out onto the freshly covered linoleum floor she'd swept earlier this morning.

We dropped abruptly to our knees, our hands frantically sweeping here and there scooping up the tiny sweets rolling in every direction across the floor. All the while, in a voice laced with righteous indignation, I complained bitterly that Roslyn had snatched the bottle from me just when I'd been about to open it . . . I'd needed no help . . . it's a good thing I'd already slackened it . . . girls are just too weak to do these things.

Now back at the window, we sucked away – two little yellow sweets at a time.

Then I tasted it.

I frowned, then hastily spat out the contents of

my mouth, for the sweets – if they could still be called that – had turned horribly bitter in my mouth.

I grimaced, stretching out a yellowed tongue. "Yuk! These sweets really strange . . . after just a few little sucks, they're getting bitter."

Roslyn nodded her agreement distractedly, her eyes fixed on the street below. "These are the worst sweets I ever tasted. Yuk! That really bitter, for true."

She spat out the chalky residue.

But come what may, we wouldn't be deprived of our bounty. Soon enough we found the technique to deal with the sweets. One by one, we sucked each one until the sweetness had worn off. Then we spat it out. Steadily we worked our way through. The bottle was soon emptied.

Like seasoned criminals, we decided it best to dispose of any incriminating evidence. The bottle went the way of the bitter residue, rattling against the concrete gutter below, bobbing up and down in the gushing water on its way to oblivion.

Later that evening, feeling unusually drowsy, I vaguely heard a puzzled-sounding Sheila saying to Mother, "I know I put them on top of the wardrobe so they'd be safe from the children. But now they're gone. I'm sure that's where I left them. I need my prescription pills."

Whether our aunt was referring to the tiny yellow sweets, or not, I feared that to own up might have some impact on Santa's generosity come Christmas day. We swore each other to secrecy.

As an extra precaution, I wagged a warning index

finger at Roslyn, threatening that if ever she were to spill the beans, she'd be in trouble. I'd tell Sheila about the swear word Roslyn had used when she'd bumped her big toe on the chair as she sat down to breakfast this morning.

Like little angels that night, perhaps slowed by the unusually drowsy feeling that plagued us both, we retired to bed early. Against the rise and fall of chirping crickets, soothing in its monotony, we hoped and prayed that our aunt would soon forget about the bitter little sweets.

We rose a little before mid-day the next day, a Saturday. Much to our relief, what happened later that day turned everyone's mind off the vanished sweets.

A red-skinned man with bloodshot eyes showed up on our doorstep with a big, seemingly heavy, cardboard box on his head. Sheila and Mother were all smiles as they greeted the man, offering him a strong-smelling drink which he quickly tossed down his throat before heaving the box up the creaky flight of stairs. He was smacking his lips when he walked out the door.

Standing on my toes, I studied with my groggy eyes the stamps clustered at the top right-hand corner of the box that stood clumsily on the drawing room floor, the Queen's head looking majestic and proud. Roslyn whispered the strange words of the return address, blending the sounds while tracing the letters with her finger.

43

A broad grin spread across her face. "Rosemary!"

"Not true!" I shouted, grinning, firmly wanting to believe, and feeling excitement exploding in the pit of my stomach.

Sheila agreed with Roslyn, and I began to jump all over the place, shouting my mother's name over and over again. Roslyn joined in, and before long we were doing a war dance to a high-tempo chant that went: 'Rose-ma-ry! Rose-ma-ry! Rose-ma-ry!'

Sheila and Mother were shaking their heads, smiling happily.

'Rose-ma-ry! Rose-ma-ry! Rose . . .'

And as our chant faltered, Sheila nodded her approval in response to the question on my face and in my pointing finger. I attacked the box, ripping into it with gusto, my drowsiness having given way to a rush of fervent energy. First I ripped off the brown string which I threw to a smiling Sheila, who wrapped it around her hand. Then I went for the sticky-tape-sealed paper, ripping it to shreds.

Roslyn and I ripped open the top flaps of the box, and found a layer of crumpled white paper; beneath that, clothes: brightly coloured tee-shirts, shorts, trousers, dresses, blouses, socks and little shirts.

Mother clapped her hands over her ears; Sheila shouted at us to stop screaming.

I pawed my way through the box, and discovered, tucked away in between the clothes, a thin envelope with red, white, and blue flashes of colour around the edges. My right index finger pointed stiffly at the envelope, another question on my face. Sheila nodded. Grinning, I took my time as I tore off the side of the envelope. The flimsy writing paper within made a crackling sound as I unfolded it and passed it to my aunt.

The adults were reading in silence; Roslyn and I were gabbling excitedly. She exclaimed how much she liked my tee-shirt with the picture of a red car on the front, all the while keeping half an eye on our aunt and grandmother, who seemed surprisingly sombre for such a happy occasion.

Roslyn was standing with her new pink dress held against her body, swinging the outfit from side to side, grinning and chuckling. I peeled off the blue tee-shirt that had yesterday protected me from the angry bull, and, despite the danger it would bring, slipped on a red jersey with a picture of a fireman on the front, the blue lights of his fire engine matching my new shorts.

Labels and plastic wrapping soon littered the floor. My sister and I swaggered around the room in an impromptu fashion parade, rhapsodising about how rich our mother was. Neither Sheila nor Mother seemed too bothered, engrossed as they were in the pages of writing-paper they held up before their eyes.

After the clothes had lost some of their fascination, I delved further into the cardboard box and surfaced, grinning, holding up a white, medium-sized box. On the bottom right-hand corner I saw a silver image of two bells that were slightly raised to the touch. Tearing open the box, I found four little packages, wrapped in shiny white paper bearing raised images of silver bells.

"What's that?" I asked, shrugging when no one answered.

The adults, still absorbed in the letter, spoke to each other in hushed tones.

I tore open the flaps of the box.

"Hey, cake!"

Roslyn scrambled to my side.

Sheila and Mother, it seemed, didn't hear. I shrugged and dug into the box.

The cake was black, with a hard outside crust that Roslyn said was icing. A minor regiment of red ants had already found their way into the box and were busy at work sampling the product. I quickly brushed them off, and tasted the cake, pronouncing it delicious. Grinning at each other, we bit through the fondant icing.

"Is there something else in there?" asked Sheila, setting the letter aside, her face taut in thought.

With a mouth stuffed full, I dived in once more and surfaced, grinning, holding up a large white book, trimmed with silver, more images of bells on the cover.

A tingle of excitement rippled through me as my imagination began to run wild. Before me opened a wondrous vision of Roslyn and me finally joining our parents in England. I called to mind the fantasies we'd so often exchanged across the room from our beds, as moonlight spilled in through the bedroom, and as sounds of chirping crickets, croaking frogs, and distant barking dogs defined the night. I recalled our animated whispers about how and when we would leave our island home; which of our treasured possessions we'd take with us on the long journey across the vast ocean; how we would frolic in the snow, build enormous snowmen, and slide down steep snow-covered hills on a gleaming red sledge. I frequently raved about the pictures I'd seen in books, of children wearing red woolly hats, gloves and scarves, and how their breath 'froze' in the air as they ran around in the snow. Roslyn rambled on about sitting on Santa's knee, pulling his long white beard, whispering her wishes in his ear. We giggled at the thought of dressing up like Eskimos. And just before dozing off, often I fantasized quietly about taking long walks along snow-speckled pavements, hand in hand with our parents.

More than once, I mused about the name I'd call my mother and father when finally I met them. I imagined they would want to be called 'Mummy' and 'Daddy'. But I wasn't sure about that. In moments of solitude, I often tried saying 'Mummy' and 'Daddy', but the sensation the words invoked made me uneasy. My aunt didn't mind us calling her 'Sheila'. I began to practice saying 'Rosemary' and 'Rodney' instead.

Only a week or two before, a friend who lived at the Quashie's – a couple of houses away – had suddenly disappeared, having gone off to England to rejoin her family. Surely our turn would be next. *I'm leaving on a Jet Plane* had played earlier on the radiogram, a good omen. Our grandmother, our aunt . . . everyone, had told us we would soon join our parents . . . soon . . . anytime soon. With the arrival of the box from Rosemary, that time must be just around the corner!

Now, perched on the settee between Sheila and Mother, sporting our brand-new clothes that smelled of England, our hands moist and sticky, my heart thumped with excitement, and I felt unable to wait any longer to see what was in the book.

Slowly, Sheila flipped over the thick, shiny white cover.

I chuckled as my eyes fell upon a picture of our mother, looking as beautiful as she did in the photo up on the drawing room wall. This time, however, she wore an elaborate white dress, cradling a bouquet in her hands.

"She looks like a princess," Roslyn breathed, sticky little fingers tracing the edge of the dress. I stared down at Rosemary's face, feeling that familiar longing, my hand drawn almost without thought to the contours of her face, drawing a brief rebuke from my grandmother.

Sheila turned over the page. Another picture of Rosemary. She was smiling and posing with two dark-skinned little girls, one on each side of her. The girls were dressed in almost identical fashion to our mother – fluffy white dresses, each carrying a bouquet.

I glanced curiously at my sister, who was frowning.

Sheila was biting her lip and shaking her head slowly, her hand distractedly running up and down Roslyn's back. I shifted my gaze back to the picture. Rosemary and the two girls were standing outside a brick church.

Slowly, thoughtfully, Sheila turned the page over. I came face to face with a picture I didn't understand at all. No fewer than ten dark-skinned men dressed in identical dark suits with dark ties and flowers on their lapels, posed outside the same brick church.

A funeral perhaps? But why were they grinning like that?

I examined their faces. None resembled my father . . . the father I remembered from the little picture in which he stood next to a bed, allowing himself a slight smile.

Sheila leafed through the album. More pictures: pictures of people surrounding our smiling mother. Everybody seemed happy.

Then I saw him.

That strange man. Always there, standing next to our mother.

Another page. My eyes fell upon a photograph of Rosemary . . . wait a minute . . . she . . . she was kissing . . . kissing that man; that strange man; that black man who in no way resembled our father. *What's going on? Why was she doing that?*

49

Then Rosemary and that short, dark-skinned man with the large flat nose, their faces wreathed in smiles . . . they . . . they were climbing into the back of a long, black car. *What was that all about? Where were they going? What sort of funeral was this?*

Totally confused, questions in our eyes, our glances flicked to each of the grownups in turn.

Why didn't Rodney appear in any of the pictures?

Sheila smiled, but couldn't mask the sadness in her eyes. Our grandmother sent us a quelling glance, raising a hand in familiar restraint, a signal we instinctively knew meant 'keep quiet and behave'.

Our bodies fidgeted, betraying us.

For what seemed an eternity, silence hung over the room.

Sheila's eyes scaled the wall to the framed picture of her younger sister. Shaking her head wistfully, our aunt sucked in a deep, shuddering breath.

Seconds continued ticking by, long seconds, eternal seconds; Roslyn and I continued to fidget. Sheila and Mother exchanged uneasy looks.

Then Sheila explained. A long, long time ago, Rodney had disappeared. Rosemary hadn't known where to find him. Our mother had tired of looking for our father; she had married . . . married another man.

No mention of Roslyn and me going to England.

CHAPTER 5

All my life I'd dreamt of setting foot on British soil. And now . . . this.

I lay there, fully clothed, curled up like a foetus on my frigid little bed, the demon trains furiously rumbling by outside my window, tormenting me in my dismal darkness. My world had caved in, and down through the black pits of despair I had plunged, dread roaring through my body, pounding in my brains, screaming in my heart, fragments of my past flashing at me . . . haunting me.

And as my thoughts spiralled, deeper and deeper I sank into the dark recesses of my mind. Dark recesses, where resided dreadful memories – awful, dreadful memories.

Again, my mind plunged back in time, the brutal memory surfacing like a monster from the deep.

"What the hell did I tell you my name is?"

Matthew's voice had hardly been raised above

a whisper, but in his bitter tone I sensed a rage that shot a bolt of fear right through my bones.

I had angered my hero.

I didn't know back then just how we were related, but, somehow, we were. He wasn't one of my grandfather's illegitimate sons who moved in and out of our rented house. We might have been related on Mother's side. But what really mattered was that he called me his little brother. Nothing else mattered. For as long as I can recall, Matthew had always lived with us – or perhaps the other way around – in the old rented house in LaClery.

He was big, and strong, and tough, and tall, and handsome, with a big round afro, and smooth light skin, only a shade or two darker than mine.

There could be no greater joy than doing things to make him happy. Roslyn and I turned ourselves inside out vying for his affection; but he always treated us equally.

Sometimes, fetching his heavy plate of food off the kitchen table, and smiling, but taking great care carrying the plate on a wooden tray upstairs and across the room to the big brown sofa in the living room, where my hero awaited, was my honoured task . . . other times Roslyn's.

Sometimes, pelting down the stairs and out through the back door to hand him a clean, dry towel as he stood outside under the cold shower, was my job . . . other times Roslyn's.

Sometimes it would be my turn to make our big brother a big glass of sweet water after he'd had an exhausting workout at the gym . . . sometimes, it would be Roslyn's.

And when he returned from work – those few times I remembered him working – he'd slump into the big brown sofa and close his eyes, resting his tired body. Roslyn and I delighted in grabbing a big, heavy leather boot each, fighting to remove it from his sweaty, smelly foot.

But one privilege was reserved only for me. Most afternoons, it would be me to scurry up the dusty Agard Hill, past the ackee tree, all the way up to the little open-air gym at the top of the hill where the cocks fought so fiercely on Sundays. From a corner of the makeshift gym in Mr. Boy's yard, I would gaze on in wonder as my hero, sweat pouring from his body, lifted the heavy weights and flexed his big bulging muscles. But the privilege went beyond that. The real privilege lay in bringing my big brother a clean, dry towel and tee-shirt, and in carrying over my seven-year-old shoulders his soaking, musky tee-shirt and towel, in full view of admiring neighbours.

My sister had no such privileges.

But today, things had been a little different.

I'd arrived at the gym right on time. When I'd shouted Matthew's name and waved the brown towel and white tee-shirt at him, he didn't answer. I shouted and waved again and again, and only stopped when he threw me a quick, quelling glare. He seemed upset about something. I wondered what it was. *Might it have anything to do with the*

53

light-skinned man followed by all eyes as he lifted weights quietly in a corner, looking bigger and stronger than even my big brother?

Half hour or so later, under bright blue skies and scorching sun, his heavy, soaking tee-shirt and towel draped over my shoulder, I had to run to keep up with Matthew as he trudged down the rocky dirt track. From behind him I watched in awe, his heavy muscles stretching the white tee-shirt to its limits. But it worried me greatly that he seemed so unusually withdrawn today. Even after I'd eagerly offered to make him a big glass of sweet water as soon as we got home, he still hadn't uttered one word to me . . . he simply kept on stomping downhill. I wondered what I had done to upset him so.

We had just passed the pit latrine in the yard when I bumped my foot and almost stumbled over a thick root growing across our path. It was a good thing Matthew didn't see that. I shuffled in subterfuge, pretending to kick an imaginary football into an imaginary goal.

We were about to go through the kitchen door when Matthew swung on his heel and, with an intense, quiet rage, stared me straight in the eyes, and then, in a voice that trembled with fury, asked that strange question: "What the hell did I tell you my name is?"

I remembered only too well how those at home had laughed at my difficulty with some words – not least Matthew's name – causing me great shame.

My heart was hammering away, not only because I feared mispronouncing the name, but because never before had I seen such anger in my hero's big brown eyes.

I felt a cold plunging sensation sweeping through my stomach. My face felt hot and my whole body trembled, as I pursed my lips in a careful attempt to utter the tongue-twisting syllables.

"Ma-ma-ma-foo?" I stammered, smiling up into the face of my big brother, hoping I had said it right.

One moment I saw his forehead wrinkled into an angry frown – the next, I glimpsed a blur flying past my face, then felt a heavy ringing thud on the side of my head, lifting me off my feet, sending me tumbling through the doorway. I landed hard on the cold concrete floor.

I lay there on my back in a kind of stupor, clutching the right side of my pulsating head, hearing a ringing sound resonating in my ears, eyeing the smoke-blackened ceiling that was spinning.

When it dawned upon me what had happened, I felt tears welling-up in the corners of my eyes. I bit my lip to push back the sob. To cry out would be weak, girlish. I knew how Matthew felt about such things. A wave of shame washed over me. Shame that I had so displeased my hero, arousing him to such anger – anger I had never before seen in him; anger that had caused him to hit me . . . for the first time. We were friends. I needed to make amends.

Before I could open my mouth to speak, I heard Matthew's angry voice break through like a clap of thunder.

"You little sissy, what's my flipping name!"

My heart thumping wildly, my eyes fled to his brown face, twisted with anger. He was bending over me, his reddened, bulging eyes inches from mine. I smelled his musky sweat, felt the warmth of his breath, felt the spittle from his snarling mouth spraying my face.

I had done enough harm. I had caused enough anguish. I needed to do better. All I had to do was say his name right . . . just once.

On trembling hands I hoisted myself up onto my bare feet, and brushed off my shorts.

I bit my lip, blinking back tears as I stared into those flaming eyes. Matthew loomed over me, his huge arms folded across his heaving, heavily muscled chest, glaring down at me, his face an angry mask.

"Ma-ma-ma-foo?" I whimpered. It just wouldn't come out right.

Through watery eyes I tried to hold Matthew's gaze, silently imploring him to give me a little more time to get it right.

A blur of the big man's fist flashed past my eyes, connecting with my chest. The force sent me tumbling backwards onto the floor in a somersault. I felt the wind knocked out of me. I gasped and heaved. Before I could regain my breath, a heavy leather sandal connected with my thigh, sending me smashing against the wooden column standing in the centre of the kitchen. Sagging under the pain, I felt as if my thigh muscle had been ripped off the bone.

When another blow banged against my skull, the rocketing pain smashed me dizzily to the concrete floor.

Still I refused to cry, as I writhed and thrashed about on the floor, legs drawn up to my chin, hands flailing frantically over my body, trying desperately to shield my chest – my head, my stomach – from the blows that now came fast and furiously.

Matthew refused to stop.

I saw flashing glimpses of my sister, my grandmother, my aunt. Dimly, I wondered how long it would be before Sheila came to rescue me. I could hear Matthew's angry voice echoing menacingly through the room, but it seemed vague and distant. The room had begun spinning. A blow to my head made it seem to explode. I writhed in pain.

I tried to bolt off, but a vicious yank of my shirt sent me tumbling back down, and earned me an even harder blow to my thigh.

"Mafoo! Mafoo! Mafoo!" I screamed, scrambling to my feet, and hobbling across the floor towards the stairs. I had to get away, to hide, until Sheila got home; otherwise, I was sure Matthew would kill me today.

I bolted up the stairs, still limping, slipping and sliding over the linoleum floor, thinking I could hide under Sheila's bed. But the big, strong, twenty-two-year-old man was at my heels, his heavy footfalls stamping on the stairs and across the squeaking floorboards. I flung myself to the floor trying to dart under the bed. A big hand grabbed my shirt and yanked me up by the scruff of my neck. The fabric cut into my chin, my feet scrabbling frantically to try and make contact with the floor.

"You little sissy, you! I'll teach you to get my flipping name right!" Matthew barked, shaking me furiously, ignoring the coughing and choking sounds coming from my throat. Struggling for air, throat burning, heart pounding, I shut my eyes tightly, vague images of Roslyn, of Sheila, of Mother, flashing before me.

With brutal rage, he went to work on my body with his heavy leather sandals; sandals with heavy metal buckles; sandals with an extra sole cut from a car tyre.

Blow, after blow, after blow.

My world began to spin furiously, carrying me down through a deep, black hole. I thought I was dreaming – and then, mercifully, I was.

My heavy eyelids fluttered, and fluttered. It seemed as if someone was trying to switch on the lights. Then the lights came on, blinding me.

My vision was blurred. I blinked and squinted to see better. Then my runny, sticky eyes saw something up above . . . a fan . . . a ceiling fan that oscillated slightly as it whirled incessantly above my head.

My whole body was one spasm of pain.

Unable to turn my head to left or right, the swirling fan held me in a trance, as it spun against the white ceiling. My aching eyes continued to blink, trying to accustom themselves to the brightness of the room. I lay there on the bed, a white sheet pulled up to my neck, every part of my body aching, my mouth dry, bitter.

A strange but not unpleasant scent invaded my nostrils; a scent not of the blossoms of the trees from the woods bordering my home, but a clean antiseptic scent. A scent that cleared my nostrils. A scent that reminded me of the medicines Sheila kept in her cabinet next to the tall wardrobe in her bedroom.

Somewhere off to my left I heard a low buzz of voices; none distinguishable; a murmuring that I felt was somehow related to me. It rose and fell as if, over and over again, someone kept reminding whoever the voices belonged to keep it down.

Is this heaven? I wondered dimly, trying to call to mind pictures I had seen in books. I felt my head growing suddenly heavy, engulfed in a throbbing ache. The room began to spin. I closed my eyes, trying to control my incessantly churning thoughts. Gradually the pain faded. The room stood still once more.

Into my line of vision came an angel . . . an angel

with short white hair, wearing a long white coat. Not only was his coat white but so too was his face. I had learned that angels were white; that Jesus was white; that all things white were good; that all white people go to heaven. I was black . . . a lighter shade of black . . . but somehow, this didn't seem like hell.

I had seen pictures of white people in books. Sometimes, from a respectable distance, people in my neighbourhood had seen them glistening on the golden sand of Malabar beach, soaking up the sun. I had never seen one in the flesh, not even from my watch tower that looked down upon the busy street. Perhaps this wasn't heaven, after all . . . but it had to be somewhere good.

The angel, heavily disguised as a white man – or perhaps the other way around – leaned down over my body, gently peeling off the white sheet. With his fingertips, horror upon horror, the angel started to prod at my chest. Wincing and grimacing in anguish, I wondered vaguely if the angel was in fact Satan – Satan had once been an Angel, Sheila had told me. So Satan must be white. This must be him . . . yes . . . it was, for it felt as if the prodding white fingers were ripping my pounding heart from my chest.

"Hello, little one," said the smiling white face. The voice was soft, and warm, and soothing. "How're you feeling? And as my body stiffened with fear, he added quickly, "Don't be afraid."

"I'm Doctor Wilson, just here to make you better.

I'll have you right as rain in no time."

Oh good. Not the devil. I stared at the white face, trying to work out the meaning of those words – *Right as rain?* – and why he spoke in that strange tone.

The white-coated man held my wrist between his index finger and thumb. He held onto it a bit longer and harder than I liked. So I tried to jerk away, but his grip was firm. I felt the blood thudding through my body, pounding in my temples. His expression changed as though he didn't like what he felt, saw, or heard.

After he had placed my arm gently back onto the bed, he pressed a rubber tube connected to his ear against my chest. When he turned away from me, I heard him speaking to someone close to my bed. "All right, tell me what happened to this child."

I heard a confused babble; people speaking all at once.

When I heard Sheila's voice I felt a calmness come over me. I was safe now. I tried to smile, but my face hurt.

Yesterday, Sheila's voice said, she had returned from work, only to find me sleeping on her bed . . . all black and blue.

Yesterday?

Then it all came flooding back, bitterly. And when I recalled just how much I'd let down my hero, I felt a sob welling up in my throat. But with grim determination, I kept the sob right down there, where it belonged . . . in my throat . . . that's where it stayed. *Big boys don't cry . . . and . . . and . . . I was no sissy.*

Then I jerked and bit my lip as a bolt of pain shot through my chest.

I clamped my eyes shut, and when I opened them I heard Mr. Rock's loud voice saying he had seen Dane and me flying down the steep hill behind the house on a sheet of Arborite. We had overshot the banks, and I landed on my chest in the dry ravine at the foot of the hill. Mr. Cox's voice agreed. Others did not. An argument broke out. The room began to spin. I closed my eyes, hoping to ease the giddiness, the throbbing pain in my head. Some time after, the room slowed, then stopped spinning.

From somewhere I heard a stern female voice, sharp in rebuke, ordering the arguing adults to keep their voices down – they were in a hospital, not the Castries fish market.

The soft-speaking doctor returned to his examination, slowly shaking his head as he leaned over my aching body. His chilly fingers traced the bones in my chest, travelling across my shoulders, and down my arms. I flinched, and flinched. Everything hurt. My whole body. Everything.

I didn't like the way he smiled down at me. He had a sad look on his face. His eyes were pleading . . . pleading me to say something . . . something about what had happened.

No way. Never. No one would ever find that out.

I was too ashamed. It was entirely my fault. All I had to do was to say something right . . . Matthew's name. I couldn't possibly tell anyone about that . . . it would only cause me more shame.

And Matthew was my hero.

Now, fourteen years later, as I lay on my bed in Lewisham, cold, and miserable, and anguished, still not a word had I uttered to anyone. Not to Sheila. Not to Roslyn. Not to Mother. Not one word about what had happened that fateful day that had caused me to remain at Victoria Hospital for all of three months.

I didn't even smile when I recalled my indignation when, on the day that I was discharged, the white-coated doctor smiled down at me, and in the same breath accused me of almost kicking the bucket. I vigorously refuted the allegation; my legs were, after all, too short to reach down to the aluminium bucket – the dust bin – under his desk.

It wasn't me who had kicked the bucket. I think it might have been Roslyn . . . she had longer legs, I remembered thinking.

CHAPTER 6

Over the years, I'd come to appreciate Charles Spurgeon's words that *many men owe the grandeur of their lives to their tremendous difficulties.*

From George Herbert, I'd learned that storms make trees take deeper root, making them stronger and better able to withstand the ravages of future storms.

The wisdom of legendary Chinese philosopher, Confucius, had taught me that *the gem cannot be polished without friction, nor can man be perfected without trials.*

I thought I'd done enough to prepare for any eventuality, for any trial or tribulation thrown my way. But now, marooned on my little bed in this frigid country, thousands of miles from the warmth of the Caribbean, I wasn't so sure. Still my eyes refused to see beyond the velvety blackness that engulfed my world. At least, mercifully, the throbbing pain that had felt like a hundred little hammers pounding away at my head had begun to subside somewhat, and the trains now passed less frequently outside my window.

I wished fervently that I could open my well-thumbed copy of *The Power of Positive Thinking* for much needed inspiration, as I'd done so many times before. My faithful companion, now withered and old, had always been there for me, ever since the fateful day I'd rescued it from a life of certain obscurity.

That miserably overcast and rainy afternoon after school, I'd found myself rummaging through a large leather trunk my grandfather had left behind. Looking for nothing in particular, somehow I'd hoped to find something ... anything. I was always looking for things. I could have sworn that Chung Li had had some treasure hidden somewhere. I'd heard so much about my grandfather who'd got his nickname from the American forces stationed in the south of the island. Word had it that the soldiers had been jovially suspicious that my grandfather's shop never seemed to run out of meat when so many other shops in the area were so frequently without. Perhaps he had turned to the stray dogs roaming the streets, something the soldiers claimed Chinese shopkeepers knew all about. The soldiers had begun to call my grandfather 'Chung Li', and the Chinese nickname had stuck.

Oftentimes I wondered about the money he had reputedly made, not only from operating rum-shops, guest houses, and grocery shops, but also from relaying to unsuspecting locals what his blind eyes had seen in his crystal ball. I couldn't figure out how he'd managed to leave the earth and his family penniless . . . utterly broke, barely able to afford the monthly house rent of twenty-five US Dollars. Perhaps he'd shared his wealth with the thirty or so outside children he'd reputedly had, some of whom he'd brought home to the care of his wife.

The old man must have left something behind . . . I kept looking.

Then I saw it. The book. A paperback, sitting alone on a pile of old newspapers in a corner of the trunk, sporting a picture of a middle-aged white man on its cover.

I picked it up, and began leafing through it. Unlikely reading though it was for an eleven-year-old, I found the faith-based philosophies espoused by Norman Vincent Peale in *The Power of Positive Thinking* deeply fascinating.

In the days that followed, I devoured the book from cover to cover, as had a good many others before me. Although I didn't know it then I had stumbled upon the inspirational best seller of all time, twenty million copies having been sold worldwide.

Perhaps I had found my treasure after all.

I tucked the book away in my makeshift library – a small bookshelf I'd hammered together from discarded pieces of wood from the nearby furniture factory.

Peale soon became my personal guru.

He had written: "Your subconscious mind . . . has a power that turns dreams and aspirations into realities when they are held strong enough. Formulate and stamp indelibly in your mind a mental picture of yourself as succeeding. Hold this picture tenaciously – never permit it to fade. Your mind will seek to deliver . . ."

This sort of thinking appealed to me. It fitted in nicely with my personal mantra picked up the year before. Mr. Combie, my primary-school headmaster, seemed always to be on a mission to inspire and motivate. Religiously during morning assembly, he presented a 'Thought for the week', which he chalked neatly on the long blackboard set high in the wall of the open assembly area. One in partic-ular stood out:

> *The heights that great men reached and kept,*
> *Were not attained by sudden flight,*
> *But they, whilst their companions slept,*
> *Were toiling onwards through the night.*

Like Contact Cement, the words set fast in my mind. I soon found myself chanting the rhyme, perhaps more often than might be considered normal for a ten-year-old.

Hard work and positive thinking – a sure recipe for success, I concluded. But it did little to alter my teacher's opinion that I wasn't ready to sit the Common Entrance examination that provided entry to one of three secondary schools on the island. Perhaps, having skipped 'Standard Three' and having been moved up to the Common Entrance class, I was disadvantaged by the gaps in my knowledge that had then begun to reveal themselves.

Another year rolled by. I took the entrance exam to St. Mary's College, the Catholic Secondary school for boys. Two years earlier, on her first sitting for St. Joseph's Convent – the Catholic secondary school for girls – Roslyn had passed; a good omen.

But I failed.

Devastated, I moped around for weeks, acting as if I wanted the earth to open up and swallow me whole. Anguish and disbelief poured through me until, in the uplifting pages of Norman Vincent Peale's bestseller, I sought and eventually found refuge and inspiration to rebound.

Yet another year passed. My term grades were good. I worked diligently. I took the exams.

Again I failed.

For weeks, bitter disappointment ate at me like acid, anguish wrapping its tentacles around me, suffocating me.

When I tried to analyse what had gone wrong, the answer eluded me. Again, Mr Peale came to my aid.

As I entered my final year of primary school, the grade reserved for those destined not to have a secondary education, I prayed for yet another shot at the elusive exam. But I would soon find out some truths about myself, so devastating that even Peale wouldn't be able to offer me comfort.

The upper age limit for sitting the exam was twelve. The school authorities requested a copy of my birth certificate, which Sheila retrieved from the Registrar's office. As she sat in the drawing room, reading the document quietly to herself, I studied her face carefully. Her expression seemed to change, from curiosity to bewilderment to horror.

After she had read through the paper several times, she sat upright, drew a long shuddering breath, and slowly expelled it. Then with her voice dropped to a sympathetic whisper, she declared that I was a year older than anyone had thought. Moreover my birthday was October 12th, not September 13th as I'd always believed it to be.

For a long, stunned moment we simply sat there, peering at this incredible document, unable to make sense of it. *How could my birthday have been so wrong for so long?* Sheila racked her brains trying to remember, but to no avail. The paper had to be correct.

Worse was to follow. Not only did the birth certificate change my astrological sign, and ruin my chances of another shot at the exam, but it even changed my identity.

Somehow, I'd always thought 'Rudy' was short for Rudolph, and I'd had to put up with a good deal of 'red-nosed-reindeer' name-calling come Christmastime. But now, according to the official, stamped and profoundly authoritative document in front of us, I was no such person. I was someone we had never heard of.

Seemingly, at the time of my birth, good handwriting hadn't been a required skill for the post of Registrar of Births, Marriages and Deaths, and the original document had been incorrectly transcribed, to read 'Reedy Radney', instead of 'Rudy Rodney'.

It was the first time I realized that I had been meant to bear my father's first name.

Now, not only did I exceed the age limit for sitting the exam, but now my schoolmates taunted me as a boy without an identity. I had neither race, nor identity. And worse still, my roots suddenly became an issue.

"How come no one had ever seen his father? Perhaps he was the product of some amorous British or American sailor sowing his wild oats on his way through the island," some suggested, in unflattering terms.

Completely disillusioned, I teetered on the brink of rebellion, frustration, and anguish, where I hovered for weeks, upsetting everyone around me, not least Sheila and Roslyn. Two years before, diabetes had struck down my grandmother; had she still been there, she too would have felt my wrath.

For months I sat in a classroom with the other unfortunates, those on the verge of leaving school with little more than a school-leaving certificate, virtually a passport to unemployment or, at best, a low-paid menial job.

Nothing seemed to make sense to me. With every fibre of my being, I believed I was destined to make something of myself, yet I was stuck in primary school feeling like an Eskimo in Africa. It made no sense . . . no sense at all. I refused to accept that fate had dealt me such a wicked, devastating blow.

One final option: the Seventh Day Adventist Academy. Privately owned and fee-paying, the SDA schools had been founded to provide for the educational needs of their members, and to promote its ministries.

I sat the exam. A marginal pass . . . entry pending availability.

A marginal pass? I couldn't fathom it. For the preceding few years I had consistently topped my every class, yet I couldn't pull out a decent pass?

There must be a higher power at work here, I thought . . . some sort of divine intervention.

Sheila went to meet the principal armed with her best persuasive manner.

And Yes. Finally. I was in. Finally . . . a secondary education.

And when, in my third year at that school, after consistently topping my class, I stood sheepishly in front of Mrs Adrian's English class, responding to the teacher's edict to make an impromptu speech on any subject, I foretold my future. "I will leave school primarily with business subjects, to prepare for a career in accountancy," I declared. "Given my late entry into secondary school, upon graduating

I'll bypass Advanced Level and head for a job at either Peat Marwick or Coopers & Lybrand, two leading firms of international chartered accountants. With a couple of years' experience under my belt, I'll head off to the UK to pursue a formal qualification. I'll return home to assume an accounting role in either the electricity company, LUCELEC, or the telephone company, C&W."

That was then, four years ago.

This was now. Now my dream had come to an abrupt, devastating end for I'd heard of blind singers, blind musicians, blind teachers, but never had I heard of a blind accountant.

Again, my spirits plummeted south, taking me deeper and deeper down into the murky depths of despair.

In the distance I heard the energetic clatter of yet another oncoming train. My body stiffened. The locomotive thundered by, roaring, shuddering, permeating my very marrow, my very soul. I kept my eyes clenched tight. No point opening them.

Gripped by a paralysing fear, I could have sworn that at any moment, the screaming, rumbling train would derail and come crashing right through my room.

Then from the dark recesses of my mind surfaced a long-forgotten memory, a vague and distant memory, a memory of the last time I had heard such frightful noise; the last time I had experienced such heart-stopping terror.

It all came flooding back.

The long and hot school holidays of 1980 had been uneventful. They had been days of reckless football and cricket in the scorching sun on the beach and on the LaClery playing field, riding ferocious giant waves in front of the Malabar Beach Hotel, and 'skanking' to 'Third World, Steel Pulse, and Bob Marley.

The blazing sun had by then conspired with the salty sea water to bleach my dense, overgrown hair a rusty red.

The usual potpourri of odours had filled the air – roasting coffee and cashew nuts, Creole cooking, burning bush, and charcoal pits, overladen always with the fresh tropical breeze from the surrounding waters – that unique island aroma.

Over a thousand miles to the east, just south of the Cape Verde Islands, a couple of insignificant thunderstorms got together, forming an area of intense low barometric pressure. Fed by the warm waters of the tropical Atlantic, they transformed themselves into that bane of the Caribbean, a tropical depression.

I continued along my carefree way, oblivious of the area of disturbed weather in conditions favourable for further development.

That sunny Sunday morning of 3rd August 1980, I had noted the unusual stillness in the air. The trees, branches, leaves, everything . . . stood still . . . completely still . . . not a flutter. Dead silence, a flat calm. The usual sea breeze had sailed away somewhere else. Overhead, a flock of seagulls flew across the sunny blue sky, heading northwards, an unusual direction for this time of year.

Meanwhile, the storm, then upgraded to a full-blown hurricane, moved westward across the Atlantic, drawing power from the seasonably warm waters beneath. In the US, the National Oceanic and Atmospheric Association tracked the path of the storm. Alarmed at its rapidly growing intensity, they issued warnings to the islands that lay in its path.

The warnings never reached me; not that it would have mattered one bit.

Granted, the year before Hurricane David had devastated Dominica. But all the same, for me the word 'hurricane' conjured up images of fun and excitement, both during the storm itself and in its aftermath.

Besides, God might very well have been a St. Lucian Himself – for as long as I'd been around, a hurricane hadn't puffed anywhere near my island.

It was Gros-Islet Day in the north. In the small fishing village, the booth-lined streets, with banners stretching across them, would be teeming with people and closed to traffic. A constant medley of hot rhythms would be blaring out from powerful, gigantic speakers, the air filled with odours of sizzling barbecue chicken, and roasting peanuts, mingled with the intoxicating scents of Heineken beer, rum punch, rum and coke, and other such beverages.

In the southern town of Vieux Fort, a carnival was about to get under way. The streets would be a riot of colour, noise and spectacle, as costumed bands paraded to the sounds of intoxicating Calypso music in the scorching heat and dazzling brightness of the afternoon sun.

Out in the Atlantic, the barometric pressure had fallen to an unprecedented low of 899 millibars, the third lowest recorded in the region since record-keeping had begun. Near its eye, Hurricane Allen packed winds of 190 miles an hour, making it a category-5 storm, the highest on the Saffir–Simpson hurricane scale.

I had donned my long-sleeved plaid shirt, tight ankle-length levis and red-laced white sneakers, and headed north to Gros-Islet.

Hours later, as the yellowing sun hovered low in the sky, then reddened as it slowly sank into the sea at the horizon, it was with a feeling of smug satisfaction that I boarded the minivan that would take me southwards along the Gros-Islet Highway, back towards home. It had been an excellent day . . . girls, girls, girls, everywhere. The only reason I had left with none of their phone numbers was simply that not having a phone at home myself it was just too embarrassing to even mention the word 'telephone'.

I watched the festivities slowly recede into the distance, a smile of smug satisfaction lingering on my lips. Though the winds had seemed stronger than usual, it had been a pretty good day. My two pals and I were in good spirits, amusing ourselves at the top of our voices, taking pot-shots at each other's chat-up lines. Indeed, the entire bus was an uproar of laughter, babbling Creole and English voices competing against the constant drone of the revving engine, as the bus lurched its way down the Gros-Islet Highway, the unusually strong winds merely accentuating the excitement.

Amid the furore, out of nowhere, a vicious gust lashed the minivan with the force of a speeding truck, sending it skidding in a zigzag path along the asphalt road, tires screeching ominously. The frail-looking red-skinned driver struggled frantically to keep control, his white-knuckled hands gripping the steering wheel for dear life, using his entire body to steer the careering vehicle back onto the road.

"Hey man," laughed one of my friends, "You hear 'bout de hurricane? 'Dis must be him on his way."

Our laughter rang out long and hard.

Visibly shaken, the driver, now seemingly in control of the vehicle, glared at us through his rearview mirror, as if to mark our faces. At that very instant, a ferocious, howling gust slammed into the left side of the minivan with an almighty bang. For a split second the vehicle became airborne before touching down and skidding out of control diagonally across the road. I heard the ominous screeching of tires, felt the rubber losing its grip on the asphalt surface, felt the momentum forcing the minivan forward, sideways, forward, sideways.

Still gripping the steering wheel, the driver managed to fight his way back on to the road, but only after the van had come perilously close to plunging into the Rodney Bay lagoon on the opposite side of the road.

Terrified passengers clung to seats, apparently willing the bus to behave, exchanging panicked glances, their laughter long since stilled.

White-knuckled, my hands gripped the back of the seat in front of me, and wouldn't let go. All around me people seemed paralysed by fear. An eerie silence hung over us.

My friends and I exchanged nervous glances. This was no joke.

For the first time in months I appealed, without moving my lips, to Jesus for mercy.

Fifteen heart-stopping minutes later, my prayer answered, I signalled to the driver to stop at the LaClery and Vigie junction, where I leapt out onto the asphalt road, all but forgetting to bid my friends goodbye. I bolted off along the Vide Bouteille Road towards home, the billowing wind tugging and shoving me this way and that, intent on ripping off my clothes, the intermittent savage gusts threatening to dump me into the thick roadside shrubbery.

Panting and weaving, I slowed to a trot as the wind gusted and the trees swayed violently above me. Leaves, plastic bags and paper bags danced furiously about. Cars parked along the roadside shuddered in the ever-strengthening gusts. In the houses lining both sides of the road, people were frantically shutting windows, locking doors, hollering out to reluctant children to get inside.

As the jalousied house with the rusty galvanized roof finally came into view in the distance, a wave of relief swept through me. *Thank you Lord Jesus*, I whispered, gathering speed now, and sprinting against the blustery winds down the hill past Raymond's grocery shop, past the Agard Hill entrance, past the Coxes' house.

I kicked away the rust-brown rock that kept the unpainted wooden door shut, then bolted indoors, where I found an angry Sheila.

"Didn't you hear about the hurricane?"

I shook my head, hand upon my chest, panting. "No."

She glanced over my shoulder, towards the door I'd left open, worry and fear etched on her face. "Where's Roslyn?"

"Think she went to the carnival in Vieux Fort." I turned to the opened door, my gaze sweeping the road for some sign of my sister.

I shrugged.

"You children have to show greater responsibility. I *cannot* do it all on my own, you know." The panic in her voice frightened me.

My aunt waved me through the house before switching on the little transistor radio cradled in her arm. "Go into the kitchen and put the groceries away."

"And leave the candles where we can find them!" she called out after me.

On the kitchen table, I found two paper bags fairly bursting with groceries: corned beef, sardines, baked beans, tuna-fish, red herring, salted fish, salted biscuits. I began to stuff them into the top shelf of the old wooden cupboard towards the back of the kitchen.

It wasn't long before my panting sister appeared in the doorway, sporting the latest tight-fitting satiny cream pants and a blue barrel top, looking as if she'd been in a fight, her 'hot-pressed' hair wild and dishevelled, her cheeks flushed.

"Where have you been?" Sheila demanded.

"Vieux-Fort Carnival."

"You two never think about anyone else but yourselves!"

Roslyn's eyes glanced my way as I reached up to shove the last tin of sardines into the cupboard, shrugging in response to her searching stare.

Several anxious minutes later we were struggling to pull the wooden windows shut against the force of incessant gale-force winds, conditions deteriorating by the second, the roof being buffeted by the ever-strengthening gusts.

Outside, I could hear strange banging noises. Unsecured bins, buckets, and other items were being tossed about in the wind, banging, rattling, thumping against the road, houses, trees, and each other.

Then the lights went out, the power cut.

After a hurried evening meal – sardines, salted biscuits, and Red Rose tea – Sheila retired to her lamp-lit room. Roslyn and I took to our single beds in the large room across the short, narrow hallway from Sheila's room. I wondered whether the fear masking her face reflected concern about her eight-year-old son riding out the storm at his father's estate in Monchy, Gros-Islet.

An hour or so later, the hurricane seemed to be at the full extent of its fury, whistling, groaning, howling, and whooshing ferociously outside, gathering speed and power. The awful, eerie sounds were unlike anything I'd ever heard, and I could only imagine that it mimicked the sound of a freight train moving at lightning speed. I marvelled that wind, so tranquil most times, could become so ravaging, so perilous, so brutal.

Bewilderment struck me anew when I realized that I'd neither seen nor heard a drop of rain. Not a single drop. I had never before considered the possibility of a hurricane without rain. This only added to the dreadful eeriness gripping me, the sinking sensation in the pit of my stomach.

Terrified to the bone, the thin sheet pulled up to my neck, I cowered in my narrow bed, praying and praying for the ferocious wind to subside. But it wouldn't let up. It only grew stronger and stronger, wreaking havoc outside, rattling, buffeting, banging the windows and doors, threatening to tear them off their rusty hinges.

With my bed set dead against the shut jalousies, without so much as an inch between, I felt every heart-wrenching gust, every shudder, every vibration; I heard every howl, every whistle, every groan, every whoosh.

And I certainly felt the howling gust that slammed the house with explosive force, shuddering the entire structure to its foundation, making my heart all but leap out of my chest. The galvanized corrugated roof rattled, buffeted, jostled violently. My heart continued racing.

Still the storm raged furiously. On and on, it kept howling, hissing, groaning, whooshing, roaring. I could hear trees bending perilously outside, branches viciously whipping the outer walls of the house as if intent on escaping the fury out there. Every so often, a loud snap penetrated the background furore, a tree or branch losing the unequal struggle against the vicious force of nature.

The battery-powered transistor radio on my little bedside table crackled with hurricane precautions and safety instructions. Then the scratchy male voice reported frantic calls flooding into Radio St. Lucia. The storm surge had begun to affect low lying areas in Dennery and Anse-La-Raye. Callers reported hearing frantic screams coming from these coastal communities, the male announcer stuttered.

My terror multiplied. The cold fear that gripped me was like nothing I'd ever experienced before. Every part of my body – muscles, joints, bone, organs – felt paralysed; my mind a torrent of confused, panic thoughts.

When the little radio died, I knew instinctively that things had taken a turn for the worse.

A few yards away on the street corner, next to the rubbish dump besides the calabash tree, the electricity pole snapped with an almighty cracking noise that sounded like a thunderbolt. Bright blue flashes lit up the room as the cable snaked menacingly across the road, casting ghastly shadows on the pale walls of the candle-lit room.

But nothing could be more terrifying than the noise now invading my mind.

For the very first time, I could hear the surf, about a mile distant, battering the shoreline of the beach, an ominous, gushing, foamy roar that grew louder and louder, as if getting closer and closer. I hadn't thought it possible to hear the winds pounding the sea against the shoreline so far off. The full horror of it struck me, and all I could think of were tidal waves . . . tsunamis.

I needed to cast the thought out my panicked mind. I closed my eyes and tried to sleep. But as soon as I tried, I saw in my mind's eye a surge of ocean water sweeping across the beach, pouring inland, mountainous torrents of foamy water heaving furiously toward our house, intent on sweeping it away. Terror impaled me. With all my might I gripped the bedding, trying to shake off the images, praying and praying with the intensity of John the Baptist. But still the wall of water kept coming and coming, sweeping through my neighbourhood, carrying debris: cars, houses, trees . . . demolishing everything in its path. Terrified, I saw Sheila, Roslyn and myself clinging together on a plank, floating away with waves crashing over us, struggling, drowning . . .

I breathed in deeply, trying to banish the terrible images, but no sooner did my ears pick up the heavy surf pounding the shoreline again than the ghastly images returned like ghosts to haunt me. Vaguely, my mind strayed to the cemetery on the beach, and to the pounding waves most likely digging up the sandy graves. Then the surging sea of water rolling towards me was littered with grisly skeletons, coffins, corpses . . .

I heard myself repeating over and over again a prayer so often recited at funerals: "Though I walk through the Valley of the Shadow of Death, I shall fear no evil. Thy rod and thy staff . . ."

Disaster seemed imminent.

I wondered about Roslyn. She hadn't uttered a word since taking to her little bed next to mine. Could she really sleep through this commotion? I envied her.

Another savage gust that jolted our side of the house sent Sheila bolting to our room, her face a mask of terror. Seeing we were safe, her hands jerked up to her chest, and with her eyes closed, heaved a huge sigh of relief, whispering something under her breath.

Roslyn sat bolt upright in bed as if abruptly

awoken from a ghastly nightmare. She asked what had happened. She had apparently thought the hurricane had long passed. Her face congealed instantly, gripped by fear.

Kerosene lamp in hand, fear still etched on her face, Sheila turned to return to her room.

She didn't get far.

A thunderous bang quaked the house to its very foundation. I could have sworn that part of the building had caved in under the impact.

Sheila stood frozen in her tracks. Roslyn leapt to her feet, terrified, looking deranged. I became aware that I was on my feet but couldn't remember standing up. My heart kept threatening to jump out, as I stood rooted in the middle of the room, shaking.

Moments later, in sudden realization, we exchanged fearful glances, turned and scrambled toward ground zero – Sheila's room. We reeled, bumping into each other at the doorway, unable to believe the awesome sight that greeted us.

Utterly agape our bulging eyeballs became riveted to the enormous breadfruit tree that had crashed through the ceiling, demolishing the entire board side-wall. All the way across the room, the enormous trunk and branches were splayed like a fallen giant. Several thick branches, complete with leaves and young breadfruits, stretched out, pressing down heavily upon Sheila's bed, where, only moments before, she had lain appealing for mercy.

"Oh my God," Sheila screamed, anguished.

Roslyn's hands shot up to her mouth . . . she sobbed uncontrollably.

I could only stand there, open-mouthed, rooted to the spot, my heart in my throat.

Then I saw it.

A gaping hole at our feet.

A thick ceiling beam had plunged through Sheila's bedroom floor, shooting down to the darkened kitchen below, shattering the board floor, leaving a hole through which an average body could easily fall. It would have been impossible for anyone in the path of the dislodged plank to have survived the impact.

I crossed myself, swallowing past the painful lump in my throat.

Outside, the ferocious howling continued to threaten our destruction. We staggered back to the relative safety of our room, but seconds later, another explosive bang. I felt the house shake free of its foundation. This time the crash came from the empty room next to Sheila's. We rushed towards it; the tall coconut tree that stood to the back of the house had been uprooted and had crashed through that side of the roof. The tree lay criss-cross atop the enormous breadfruit tree that protruded through Sheila's room. Two uninvited guests.

We exchanged frantic glances, as if sensing our imminent demise.

I wanted the torment over and done with, quickly.

Paralysed by fear, I felt helpless against the monster that hadn't yet tired of howling, growling, whistling, whooshing . . . ferociously. We stood little chance against this monstrous force of nature. I wasn't sure whose side God was on. Why did the monster keep tormenting us? Why couldn't it just end everything now . . . right now? I felt completely at its mercy.

Almost in slow motion, Sheila laid her weary body down onto the empty bed in our room.

Shivering in my own bed, I awaited the inevitable.

Allen still raged furiously on, never-ending. I kept praying and praying. The winds kept howling and howling. Trees kept snapping and snapping.

Slowly, as the night passed, rays of light began to streak through the crevices in the wooden jalousies, ushering in the dawn. Tentacles of light criss-crossed the floor, superseding the shadows that had surrounded us all night.

No roosters crowed that morning, no . . .

The clicking sound of keys in the door lock of my London lodging invaded my thoughts, rousing me back to the present. Heart pounding from the memory, I returned to my pitiable state. I would gladly have traded the dark and dismal reality that I now faced for a hurricane or two – even a hurricane with its eye passing directly overhead, unlike Allen.

At least St. Lucia had recovered from the devastation, and so had our house; much more than I suspected I'd be able to say of myself in my current predicament.

CHAPTER 7

I heard the key turn in the lock and my landlord's footsteps walking heavily across the carpeted board floor.

I remained lying there on my bed, not wanting to face the man, or anyone else for that matter.

I wasn't sure whether it was shame, or pride, or guilt, or a combination of all these, washing over me like a tidal wave. Whichever it was, I felt too low in spirit, too weak of heart, to muster the mood or inclination to interact with anyone, to say nothing of reaching out for help.

I had no clue of the time. Not normally home during the day, I knew nothing of my landlord's work schedule. It could have been midnight for all I knew, or cared.

Dizziness still hazed my head, but the throbbing pain in my forehead had retreated to an ache on the periphery of my mind, still present but bearable now.

I opened my eyes slowly, cautiously. Blackness.

I knew by now, it wasn't the blackness of the night. Despair was eating away at me like a cancer.

I could hear my landlord whistling a happy little tune through his teeth as he moved about the house. On the floor above my head, I heard the gushing sound of a flushing toilet. Then the wooden stairs creaked and creaked under his ample weight as he made his way downstairs. When he creaked past my room, I faintly recognised the tune he so merrily whistled – 'Saltfish' by The Mighty Sparrow.

The creaking footfalls continued all the way down to the basement kitchen.

I willed him to switch on the central heating as he moved about down there, for I felt chilled . . . chilled to the bone, much the same as I'd felt on the bus earlier that morning. The frigid wind from outside seemed to seep through the invisible cracks in the concrete walls of my room, creating a chilly penetrating draught.

Perhaps my landlord had gone downstairs to prepare dinner? A lonely, solitary dinner, I thought vaguely. Save for the occasional visit from his teenage daughter, he never seemed to have any female company – or, for that matter, any company at all. He seemed a lonely soul. No wife, no girl-friend, no one.

In my darkness, my thoughts wandered to the girl of my dreams; the girl I'd been envisioning to escape the gloom that seared my heart, devouring my mind. The most beautiful girl in the world. Tucked between the pages of my thin 1984 diary, I kept a small picture of her . . . a picture that I turned to most nights . . . my source of motivation and inspiration. It mattered little that she knew nothing of the way I felt, or of the plans I had for her. Destiny was destiny, I'd always told myself; destiny will deliver her in time.

Now, in my gloomy plight, I wondered whether I'd ever again gaze upon her lovely picture, let alone herself in the flesh.

It was four years previously that we'd met. The first week of the new school term; the year after Hurricane Allen had all but flattened St. Lucia.

At midday, the morning-shift students were making their way home, giving way to the lower graders in the afternoon shift. The shift system had solved the school's space problem.

Free for the rest of the afternoon, with exhilarating blue skies, luminous sunshine, and a constant sea breeze, I felt it was a perfect day for the beach. A five-minute walk from the highway was all it would take to get to Halcyon Beach.

But the four of us, uniformed in black trousers and white shirts that were unbuttoned half way down our chests, had more pressing matters to deal with . . . more exciting pursuits. With a keen sense of anticipation, we loitered at the front of the school, or rather, the back that served as the front, busy feasting our eyes on the new crop of female recruits making their way into school.

We rated them on a scale from one to ten. Soon

enough we broke into heated argument about the inconsistencies inherent in our scoring system. One or two asserted that the loose-fitting uniforms didn't do justice to the girls' figures; another was adamant that the very notion of not being able to see what the girls would look like beneath the thick fabric of their green uniform provided the real excitement, and as such should attract higher scores.

Then my eyes wandered off.

And, straight ahead in the distance, I saw her.

My heart jolted as if I'd stumbled on a rock in my path.

I swallowed hard.

When I opened my mouth to speak, it was not to refute my querulous friend's claim that St. Joseph's Convent had by far the most beautiful girls on the island; it was simply to utter, quietly, in awe, just one word: "Jesus!"

My mind blanked as I watched the young lady stride gracefully across the parched field, making her way towards the bottom of the stairs where we stood. Her green and white uniform seemed a perfect fit.

Faster and faster my heart kept racing and racing, as she moved closer and closer. My face was growing steadily warmer. I didn't need a mirror to know I had turned bright red.

She strode elegantly, with the dignified, vertical posture of a fashion model, but seemingly without any kind of conscious effort. Her long jet-black curls contrasted with her light skin, radiating an intriguing combination of youth, innocence, sophistication, beauty.

I hardly knew how it happened, but I found myself standing before her, my gaze riveted down upon her lovely face, feeling the warm glow of adrenalin rushing through me.

A nervous smile played on my lips as I stood there with my thumbs tucked into the tags of my corduroys, my heart pumping faster and harder than ever. Then I cleared my throat, and strode for a deep macho voice. "Hi, I'm Gurley . . . what's your name?"

She hesitated a moment, then responded with downcast eyes. "Susanna."

"You're pretty," I said to her long, lush, ebony curls glistening in the bright sunlight.

An embarrassed blush began to surge through her cheeks and neck. "Thanks," she said demurely, flicking me a glance, and immediately dropping her gaze once more to the parched grass at her feet.

After an awkward silence, I said, "So . . . umm . . . how old are you?"

"Thirteen."

There was only a slight tremor in her voice.

I brushed off the sweat beading my forehead, while scouring my brains for something interesting to say.

"Uh . . . uh . . . amm . . . what's your name again?"

"Susanna."

Transfixed, I stared at her as she stood against

the backdrop of lush green vegetation across the road.

"Susanna what?"

"Ramjeawan."

"Run Joe Run?"

She smiled for the first time, revealing unsuspected dimples in both cheeks.

"No . . . Ram-jea-wan," she said slowly.

I gazed at her face in stunned delight, and over the next thirty seconds did my utmost to provoke the dimples' reappearance.

Failing miserably, I soon ran out of words. Not a word, not a phrase, could I recall from my repertoire of chat-up lines that filled a hard-covered notebook tucked away in my bag. They had all fled my mind. Small talk, nothing talk . . . it all deserted me. Like a flash in a pan I fizzled away. I simply resorted to staring sheepishly at her gorgeous face, seeing the sunlight glinting in her curly hair, gilding it with an elegant sheen, and turning her luminous eyes a sparkling bronze.

Then I felt my hand lifting to brush away a lock of hair that had blown across her smooth cheek. The quick backward movement of her head brought me back to my senses. After the awkward silence that ensued, I told her how nice it was to meet her.

She thanked me, smiled shyly and turned to walk away.

As I gazed at her upright retreating back, as certain as the pounding of my heart, as certain as the scorching sun bearing down its fury upon us, I knew she'd be the one.

My mind was made up.

It wasn't long before I learned that Susanna's father was of East Indian descent; her mother, a fair-complexioned Negro.

Later that afternoon, the warm glow of euphoria consumed me as I made my way home on the bus, Susanna's smiling, dimpled face monopolizing my thoughts.

When I arrived at the medium-sized house at Morne-du-Don, the rented house that had become my home since Hurricane Allen, I relaxed a while on the balcony wall. My legs were outstretched before me as I leaned back against the thin metal pole. My eyes took in the panoramic view of Castries down below in the distance, nestled between the base of the rolling green hills and the endless expanse of the sparkling blue water. The scorching afternoon sun glinted off rooftops.

But instead of taking in the landscape, my mind played and replayed scenes of a veiled Susanna gracefully striding down the aisle in an immaculate, flowing white dress, arm-in-arm with her father, taking their cool time, marching slowly to 'Here Comes the Bride' . . . marching towards *me* as I stood in my three-piece suit at the front of the packed church, waiting . . . waiting with a thumping heart.

Every night, since then, lying in bed, I would see my future unfolding before my mind's eye.

Norman Vincent Peale had taught me that:

An image formed and held tenaciously in the conscious mind will pass into the unconscious mind. And when it is accepted firmly in the unconscious, the individual will tend to have it, for then it has you . . . A long held visualisation of an object or goal can become determinative.

I believed.

From that point on, I did my utmost to impress Susanna at school, not least when we senior boys played cricket in the scorching heat on the parched field, with the girls lining the veranda up above, gazing down upon us.

I couldn't stop glancing up her way, more than ever when I posed at the crease and played an ostentatious forward defensive stroke, or hit the ball stylishly off the back foot. Once, my gaze lasted a bit longer than usual, and Susanna waved ever so slightly and sent me the sweetest little smile I'd ever seen. *Yes! Good progress!*

With Susanna several grades below me, though, and with my inbuilt shyness, only occasionally did we get to speak.

Finally, one day I could take it no more.

I made my move.

I looked up her number in the telephone directory.

I picked up the phone.

I dialled.

I waited.

The line began to ring.

One ring . . . two rings . . . three . . . four . . . five rings.

My heart pounded.

I waited, hearing the crickets chirping, riding the sound of the early evening.

The phone kept ringing and ringing; my heart kept pounding and pounding.

Both relieved and frustrated, I was about to hang up when I heard the phone click. Then a grown-up female voice said, "Hello."

I hesitated.

"May I . . . I speak to Susanna, please?"

A brief silence greeted these words. Then the voice spoke again. "Just a moment. Who is it calling?"

I did not reply immediately. "A school friend."

I heard muffled conversation going on in the background.

Then I heard Susanna's voice, shaky, uncertain, "Hello?"

My heart skipped a beat. I paused, sucking in a deep rush of air.

"Hello?"

"Hi Susanna, this is Gurley . . . from school."

Silence ensued. Then her voice said, "Gurley?"

"Yes . . . from school."

Silence.

Then I heard the adult female voice say something in the background; I couldn't make out the words.

Susanna's shaky voice came through. "Gurley . . . Mum says that I'm not old enough to have boyfriends. She says that I have to wait until I'm out of school, so please don't call me again."

In the silence that ensued I felt as if the carpet had just been yanked out from under me.

"I don't want to get into any trouble," Susanna's voice said.

Feeling that swooping sensation in my gut, I whispered a quick apology, and a cheerful goodbye, happy she couldn't see my reddened, sweat-dampened face.

With a heart sullen from the veto, I looked out the window at the sky that seemed overcrowded with twinkling stars, stretching to eternity.

Then I heard my voice humming Bob Marley's song about not wanting to wait in vain for your love.

Back in London, my memories fled as I heard the hollowed rumble of a plastic object dropping to the floor in the basement kitchen.

The vision of Susanna faded, as had my dreams earlier today.

My mind returned to its present pitiable state.

Downstairs, I heard my landlord pottering around in the kitchen, perhaps cooking-up that solitary meal.

What now? I thought. Was it all over for Susanna and me? Had I lost her along with my other dreams?

CHAPTER 8

1983 had come quickly.

It was the year that I graduated at the top of my class, and convinced Coopers & Lybrand, Chartered Accountants, that although I was bypassing the Advanced-Level College to make up for lost time I deserved a shot as a junior auditor.

But that wasn't at all the highlight of my year. Neither was America's invasion of the tiny island of Grenada. My highlight was, pure and simple, a telephone call. A simple little telephone call.

That Saturday afternoon, the sun blazed relentlessly, its presence felt even in the darkest of shades. Cumulus clouds, rolling fluffy and white, drifted steadily under the solid blue sky, pushed along by the constant trade winds flowing from the east.

Stretched out on the fluffy sofa in the sunny living room at Morne-du-Don, I raked my brains trying to make sense of Boy George's 'Karma Chameleon' blaring from the speakers in the corner of the living room. I had just about concluded that his reference to 'red, gold and green' probably indicated some affiliation with the Rastafarian movement, when I thought I heard, piercing the music, the persistent ringing of the telephone.

I scrambled to my feet, raced across to the counter dividing the living and dining rooms, and snatched up the receiver.

"Hello."

"Hello . . . may I speak to Rudy?"

The female voice, with an odd inflection, rang no bells.

"Yes, this is Rudy."

The silence that ensued was long. Uncomfortably long.

Then the voice ventured a question.

"Hi Rudy, how are you?"

"Fine, thank you. And you?"

"I'm fine."

In the void that followed, I gazed out absently through the sliding glass doors at the sprawling mango tree bordering the neighbouring property, wondering vaguely when next it would be laden with fruit.

The voice spoke again. "Do you know who you're speaking to?"

I searched my mind. "No . . . not really."

Another silence.

"This is a call from England."

England? Who could be calling me from England?

"OK."

A long silence greeted that word.

"It's your mom."

My heart jolted as if I'd missed a step going downstairs. "Who?"

The voice hesitated. "Your mother . . . Rosemary."

Those words hit silence. I felt my pulse quickening as the words resonated in my head, bouncing off the walls of my cranium, before finally registering with sobering reality.

"Sorry, who . . . who did you say you are?"

"Rosemary . . . your Mom."

My heart was pounding hard and fast.

With slightly trembling hands, I pulled up a chair and took a seat at the dining table, conflicting thoughts tumbling around in my mind, bouncing off each other.

'It couldn't be – yes it could – she didn't say, 'Rosemary, your Mum' – yes she did. Perhaps someone's playing a trick.

"Rosemary?" I said, in a disbelieving tone, feeling the tension on the line.

The voice didn't answer right away. But finally, it said, "Yes . . . your mother."

I felt excitement exploding in the pit of my stomach. For a brief instant, I could find no words to speak; I could only think them.

Rosemary . . . my long-lost mother . . . was on the line to . . . to me?

I closed my eyes, then reopened them slowly, sucking in a long and deep but quiet breath, then releasing it slowly.

Rosemary?

Then I heard four simple words issue from my lips. "Hi, how are you?"

The neutral accent again hesitated, then: "I'm fine." Another pause. "Are you surprised to hear from me?"

"A bit," I lied.

I wasn't surprised. I was flabbergasted.

After yet another brief pause, she said, "Well, things have been difficult for me, you know, but I never forgot you and Roslyn."

"That's OK." *What else could I say?*

An awkward silence, then, "Did you get the clothes that I sent you all?"

I searched my mind. Then I found the clothes. I believe I had been five – or was it six? – when we received that package.

"Yes, thank you."

That awkward silence again.

"You sound so grown-up . . . you sound like a grown man."

"Thank you."

"How old are you now?"

"Just turned twenty."

"Wow . . . funny how time flies." Pause. "So what do you do for a living?"

"I'm a junior auditor at an international firm of chartered accountants – Coopers & Lybrand – I'm training to become a professional accountant."

"Wow. That's good. I mean . . . I always knew you'd do well. I'm so very proud of you." She paused. "Sheila did a very good job."

"Yes . . . she did."

As the conversation drifted along in that loose, disjointed manner, more than once I pinched my arm, hard. The stinging red welt on the inside of my left forearm proved irrefutably that I wasn't dreaming. *Thank God!*

As we spoke, my state of mind turned gradually from bewilderment, through to intrigue, then to sheer delight. A smile kept dancing upon my lips as I pulled up another chair, over which I stretched my bare legs. I leaned back, the telephone receiver pressed to my ear, listening to her . . . listening to Rosemary . . . listening to my mother . . . I couldn't believe it!

She had remarried. Her second husband, formerly of Trinidad and Tobago, held a PhD in economics.

I could have sworn I heard her voice falter when she mentioned that she'd last seen Rodney back in 1964 – the last time she'd lain eyes on my father.

As our conversation drifted to Roslyn, I heard a metallic-sounding disembodied female voice prompting for more coins to be inserted into the slot.

Then the line died.

Rosemary called back.

We continued our hesitant conversation.

Later that evening, unable to sleep, and after I'd infected Sheila and Roslyn with my excitement, my opportunistic mind turned to the possibilities now opening up to me. When, in 1981, I'd declared my

101

intention to pursue studies in the UK, Rosemary hadn't featured at all in my reckoning. The timing of her call astounded me – nothing less than an act of divine intervention, I concluded.

Then came her letters, professionally typed and educated in tone. I was suitably impressed.

When I divulged my plans to pursue studies in England, she readily volunteered to provide me with boarding and lodging at her home in Milton Keynes, a commuter town fifty miles north of London. My heart leaped in joy. A major problem had been solved.

The other major problem, yet unresolved – the cost of tuition.

As fate would have it, I soon found myself on an auditing assignment at the St. Lucia Development Bank, which, I learned, offered student loans. Two weeks later I sat in the Managing Director's office, signing documents for a two-thousand-pound loan – the maximum available without property or cash as security. Sheila and Roslyn signed as guarantors, rendering themselves liable in the event I defaulted. I hadn't a clue where the remaining seventy per cent of tuition fees would come from.

But no matter, I would get by somehow.

I began to save every penny of my one hundred and fifty pounds' monthly salary, withdrawing my contribution from the household finances, throwing an increasing burden on my sister and aunt, who remained totally supportive. Three years before,

Roslyn had graduated from St Joseph's Convent and had found a job at the Canadian Imperial Bank of Commerce.

In mid-December 1984 I resigned my job, bought a ticket to the UK, and packed my bags.

But everything changed when, seven days before my planned departure, another letter arrived from England.

Eagerly I had opened it.

But the words that I read hit me with almost physical force, threatening to send me to my knees. Sweat dampened my body as my slightly tremulous hands reached out for the nearest seat. I read the letter through twice in quick succession, a thousand conflicting thoughts and emotions whirling through the chaotic turbulence that my mind had instantly become. Then sweat began pouring down my body as the house settled into silence around me – a deep, gloomy, crypt-like silence.

The rug had surely been yanked from under my feet, and now I was spiralling head-first down into the dark, dismal abyss of uncertainty, of gloom, of despair, my blood pressure rising, my heart pounding, my brain exploding in outrage.

I couldn't believe the words my eyes had read.

Feeling disappointment burning in my throat, I crumpled the letter into a tight little ball, shoved it into my trouser pocket, and decided on a walk to calm myself, my nerves.

I must have looked like death as I walked slowly and miserably down the Morne-du-Don Road. I became distinctly aware of the dirty sky that hid the sun, turning the day dark and dismal, deepening my gloom. I returned home three sober hours later, under a fine, clean drizzle, and told no-one of my looming predicament. Calmly but pensively, I continued my preparations for departure.

Then I sat down, penned a letter of my own, addressed it, sealed it, stamped it, mailed it.

My plans had remained unchanged.

CHAPTER 9

To the air-traffic controllers monitoring its progress across the Atlantic on 3rd January 1985, the British Airways aircraft would be known as 'Speedbird 0071'.

With gloomy trepidation, from inside the crowded departure lounge, I peered out through the large glass panel, surveying the preparations for departure. Shifting uncomfortably in my seat, I allowed my eyes to follow fuel trucks, baggage carts and sundry technicians all swarming around the colossal machine.

In no way did it help my nerves that Lord Kelvin's forceful pronouncement kept resounding ominously in my head:

'Heavier-than-air flying machines are impossible,' the 19th-century president of the Royal Society had said.

Notwithstanding evidence to the contrary, my mind couldn't fathom that this monster would really lift off from St. Lucia's Hewanorra International Airport and, eight hours later, touch down at a predetermined spot four thousand miles across the Atlantic.

Catching sight of the flight crew casually sauntering through the lounge on their way to the aircraft served only to heighten my anxiety. Somehow, I'd expected the pilot of such a machine to be a magnificent gentleman: tall, broad-shouldered, lantern-jawed. But it was not to be. To my utter dismay, the captain, four bands of gold braid on his white jacket, seemed unremarkable: short, with narrow shoulders, thinning grey hair, a thin, sharp face. Even worse, talking animatedly at the top of his voice, he appeared to be sharing a crude joke with his crew, who responded with fits of laughter. Such unwonted levity seemed hardly befitting to one about to undertake a death-defying flight across the ocean, I thought.

Such is the paranoia of the first-time traveller.

My panic-stricken eyes scanned the departure lounge. People everywhere: seated – seated on the cold tiled floor, seated on colourful plastic chairs; standing – standing alone, standing in small knots of two or three, lost in conversation; and yet others milling around in and out of duty-free shops (the one or two there were), picking up last-minute souvenirs. Most were English holidaymakers apparently returning home from a winter break. A scattering of dark-skinned faces, mostly locals, I imagined, probably off to visit relatives, or perhaps returning UK residents. I wondered how many, like me, were about to embark on a course of study, submerging themselves into the dreaded cold in the depths of an English winter.

One passenger clearly wasn't a student. The

wizened little dark-skinned man, dressed in an over-sized baby-blue three-piece suit with a loose, lopsided, red bow tie, sat quietly cradling to his chest a large black plastic bag, his moist, red eyes blinking and blinking, staring into oblivion. With a tinge of sadness, I wondered who, if anyone, had come to see off the man who seemed a lost and lonely soul.

Finally, with a muffled announcement over the PA system, the interminable wait was over. A fine-looking dark-skinned lady, in a tight black skirt and blue cardigan, led the assembled passengers briskly across the tarmac to the waiting machine. I approached the Boeing 747, marvelling at its sheer size. With foreboding, my mind again flashed back to Lord Kelvin's pronouncement on heavier-than-air flying machines, and very quickly I found myself buying into his doom-laden logic.

"God help me," I whispered, quickly making the sign of the cross, twice.

All but forgetting, I wheeled around and waved a last nervous goodbye to Roslyn, Sheila, and Jonny, Sheila's twelve-year-old son, barely noticing in the dim light their frantic waves from the balcony of the terminal in the distance. Like a modern-day Jonah, I then disappeared into the belly of the great flying machine.

I fought my way down the aisle, past lobster-red faces. Everywhere, passengers were trying desperately to stuff oversized packages into stubbornly protesting overhead lockers. Finding my allocated seat at the far end of a centre row, I squeezed in between a deeply tanned shaven-headed man in a Hawaiian shirt, and a little old lady with heavy, mud-like foundation and bright red lipstick. A complicated set of buttons in my armrest kept me occupied for a minute or two. Failing to master them, I turned my attention to the safety-instruction card in the seat pocket in front of me.

Packages safely stowed, passengers strapped in, I heard the roar of the engines as Speedbird 0071 began its slow trundle towards the departure point.

My pulse began to race.

In accordance with the time-honoured tradition of the airline industry, the flight attendants then took the opportunity to intensify the paranoia of their passengers, by running through safety demonstrations. As instructed, I followed them along on the safety card, and quickly came to the conclusion that the whole thing would be a complete waste of time were, God forbid, a disaster to strike – I couldn't see how any of this would save any of us. The colourful illustration of happy people gaily waving from their inflated life raft seemed merely a polite fiction, a wicked little voice in my head whispered to me.

I did, however, feel beneath my seat for my life jacket, thinking the while that a parachute would have been more appropriate, and certainly more comforting.

Safety drill done with, the smiling flight attendants took to their seats. Casting an assurance-seeking glance at them, what I observed left me feeling anything but reassured. They had strapped themselves into their seats, harnessed not just with a lap strap as were the passengers, but also with shoulder straps. *Did they know something that we, the passengers, didn't?* The sweat on my brow began to make its way past my temples.

The roaring boom of the engines intensified as the plane started its take-off roll. I clenched my eyelids shut, and prayed. *"God help me . . . please, please, please."*

I would have prayed even harder had I known then that, despite Lord Kelvin's forceful prediction, the assembled bits of metal, rubber and plastic that I sat in, weighing some three hundred and fifty metric tonnes, required a forward speed of some two hundred miles an hour to overcome the force of gravity.

As the rumbling grew louder and louder, I felt despite the cool of the air-conditioning, my entire body become dampened with sweat, my heart pounding brutally.

The old man in the three-piece suit, sitting two rows down the aisle from me, hunched himself into the approved 'brace position' for crash landing.

My knuckles whitened from the force of gripping the armrest.

The aircraft sped down the runway, the vibration intensifying, the boom deafening. My eyes flew open and, to my horror, the overhead storage bins seemed to have come alive, and were dancing a furious Spanish fandango. Surely something would fall apart soon! But my primary concern was whether we'd have lift-off at all.

In my frenzied state, I found myself condemning my every decision of late; every decision that had served to bring me to this point in my life – tied down in an enormous bullet that was shooting down the runway. Suddenly, my decision to quit my job, to buy that ticket, to want to become an accountant, all seemed totally asinine.

Too late now. I braced myself, eyes clenched tight once again, body stiffened.

Then, miraculously, and to my heart's relief, the rumbling suddenly ceased and the vibration decreased as the aircraft lifted off, the engine noise lessening as the plane climbed up and away, up through the evening clouds, away from my island home.

But the sigh that I breathed was faint and shallow, for I sensed, up ahead, more heart-stopping terror.

"Would you care for a drink, sir?"

A flight attendant's face was smiling down at me soon after the 'Fasten seat belts' sign had blinked off. Never before had I the privilege of being served by a white person, to say nothing of being called 'Sir' by one.

In her glorified purplish house-dress of a uniform, the slightly overweight brunette confounded my image of an air hostess. Somehow, I'd expected a sophisticated blonde bombshell, as depicted in magazines and on television. Her bright smile and cheerful manner, however, more than compensated for her average looks.

"Er . . . a vodka, please."

"Straight up . . . or on the rocks?

"A little ice, please."

That pleasant smile still lingering on her lips, she set out a paper napkin on my tray table, onto which she gently placed the screw-top miniature bottle of vodka and a packet of pretzels.

"And would you like red or white wine to go with your meal, sir?" she smiled, adding, "The menu's in the pocket in front of you."

I opted for something called Chicken Kiev, and for **red w**ine.

"That's what I'm having, too!" the petite old white woman sitting next to me chimed in, smiling up at me, revealing a perfect set of teeth that clicked comically, exposing their false nature.

I struck up a conversation with the cheery old woman with jet-black hair greyed at the roots, and who, despite her heavy makeup, had crows-feet wrinkles deeply etched into the loose skin around her pale blue eyes and at the corners of her thin, bright red lips.

She talked about her life, now and then placing a blue-veined, wrinkled hand on my arm, not least when she mentioned her grandchildren or spoke fondly of the friendly people she'd met on the island. Ever so often my gaze dropped to the bony hand resting on my arm. The joints of her fingers were swollen; the fingertips bent forward, clawing away at nothing.

As she prattled on, I couldn't help thinking how,

111

for the past week, I'd hoped to be nestled next to an attractive young female for the eight-and-a-half-hour journey. But with her charm, good humour, and engaging manner, my companion soon cast aside my initially grave disappointment.

"Your island is so beautiful," she rhapsodised. "It's been the best holiday of my life. All you people are so warm and friendly, I hate to leave. I'd been promising myself a holiday ever since my husband died ten years ago. Now my children barely bother to come and see me, so I thought I'd go off somewhere warm and nice for Christmas. You know, my arthritis bothers me so, what with the weather in England, so damp and cold at this time of year . . ." She sighed resignedly, shifting slightly in her seat, wincing with some unmentioned discomfort.

She rattled on as if I'd be the last person she'd speak to in a long time, barely leaving an opening for me to slip in a monosyllable or two. Much to my relief, the interaction went some way to taking my mind off the terrors of the flight. For the life of me, I couldn't fathom how anyone could feel so much at ease, as though it were an everyday occurrence, suspended as we were thirty five thousand feet above the dark ocean in a big tin tube. It was then that I realized I'd developed a new skill, for with one ear I was able to listen to the lady, while the other monitored the booming engine.

A female flight attendant, much to my relief, materialized with the Chicken Kiev, red wine, and chocolate cake. I had spotted the single male steward working his way along the opposite aisle. He had a somewhat effeminate air about him. His bleached blond hair, with a quarter-inch of black at its roots, glistened under the cabin lights, remaining fixed, unmoving, as if held in place by layers of hairspray. As he wiggled past, smiling at me, a mixture of lacquer and flowery cologne assaulted my nostrils, leaving an unpleasant taste in my mouth. I felt easier in my mind that the ladies were the ones attending to me . . . and they kept the drinks flowing too.

The meal over, the cabin lights were dimmed for the night crossing. My little old friend nodded off.

Left to my own uninterrupted thoughts, my mind and ears became better attuned to the mechanics of the flight, picking up every slight variation in the boom of the engines. I remembered only too well the many times I'd seen motor vehicles stall mid-journey, right there in the middle of the road. My mind could find no logical reason why an aircraft shouldn't suffer a similar fate, and drop like a rock down to the dark shark-infested waters below.

Just one loose screw or bolt is all it would take I heard myself thinking, over and over again, as my fingers gripped the armrest tighter and tighter. With tensed shoulders, I stiffened in my seat sensing a certain premonition of dread that mounted with each passing second.

It seemed hours before the red wine and vodka began to take effect. A warm, glowing sensation now consumed me, my eyelids heavy, drooping as if reinforced with a layer of lead.

Then I felt a sudden jolt that surged right through the cabin. Then another. And another.

I heard passengers gasping; a child screaming. My heart began to thump hard and fast, warm blood rushing to my head, a sickening wave of giddiness engulfing me.

On came the 'Fasten seat belts' sign.

Flight attendants were scurrying unsteadily up and down the aisle, gripping the back of seats, checking passengers were safely strapped in.

"Ladies and gentleman," the captain's disembodied voice sounded through the cabin, "We are experiencing some air turbulence. Please return to your seats immediately, and fasten your seatbelts."

The shuddering through the cabin grew stronger and stronger, and louder and louder. I felt weaker and weaker. The little old lady grabbed my arm as I hastened to tighten my seat belt, steeling myself for our seemingly inevitable fate.

A few rows down, an overloaded locker flew open, spilling its contents out across the cabin. More screams. The 'Fasten seat belts' sign kept blinking. Eerie beeps sounded throughout the cabin. The old man in the three-piece suit remained hunched forward in the brace position.

I could have sworn the aircraft was about to break up; only a matter of time before the wings snapped.

God help me!

Then I felt a sinking sensation in my gut, a feeling of weightlessness, as if the plane was dropping out of the sky like a stone. Screams grew louder, and more frequent; the plane continued to lose altitude rapidly.

Another violent jolt, and now it felt as if a powerful force was tugging the aircraft up and up again. Frantically, I bargained with God, pleading for the jostling, the shuddering, the sickening noise, to stop.

The pilot seemed to have lost control. I dangled from the edge of my seat. All around me I heard the cries of women, the screams of children, and the gruff, terrified voices of men. All around me I saw looks of terror. Lost, terrified faces . . . faces like mine.

Frantically, my eyes searched the faces of the flight attendants for some sign of comfort, some sign that they had seen it all before, that this was no big deal, that it would soon pass.

But in their eyes I saw only fear, only panic.

I resigned myself to fate. I had no choice in the matter, paralysed as I was with fear, incapable of movement.

Suddenly, eerily, everything seemed to be moving in slow motion – slow, slow, slow motion, as in the movies. I knew the end was near.

Then I heard a loud bang, and with a start my eyes shot open. I sat bolt upright in my seat. My gaze jerked down to an attendant stooping in the aisle a few feet down from me. She was smiling pleasantly, picking up off the floor what seemed to be a bottle of wine, a bottle that must have dropped from her tray.

I shook my head vigorously. *Was I dreaming?*

For a long stunned moment I remained motionless, silent, my mind a jumble of frenzied thoughts, my bewildered eyes scanning the cabin. Lights were dimmed. People seemed peacefully at sleep. The little old lady's head rested snugly on my shoulder. I took a deep, shuddering sigh of relief, feeling the tightness in my chest loosening. My right hand hurriedly made the sign of the cross.

Thank God . . . only a dream.

Though I felt immensely relieved, my nerves continued to simmer with dread. *Had I just had a premonition? Had I just seen what was about to happen?* That wicked little voice in my head just wouldn't let up.

Vodka and red wine and heavy eyelids notwithstanding, I had no intention of shutting my eyes for the remainder of the journey.

As Speedbird 0071 roared across the Atlantic towards England, I felt other traces of doubt and dismal thoughts welling up in the back of my mind.

I rummaged through my carry-on bag, extracted a creased white envelope, pulled out a crumpled sheet of paper and smoothed it out.

But didn't read it. I shoved it right back into the bag. I still couldn't bring myself to stop thinking about the words that had all but floored me when first I'd read the letter seven days before. In formal language, Rosemary had explained how difficult things were in the UK. With the entire country in the throes of a deep recession, no longer was she able to accommodate me at her home. I should remain in St. Lucia. No point coming to the UK.

Just like that. Just like that. Stay home? Forget about the UK? After I had resigned my job, bought my ticket, made all preparations? Stay home?

The letter I'd scratched and mailed to my mother pulled no punches. One paragraph in particular echoed ominously in my mind:

I will be coming to the UK – as planned. All I require is boarding for three weeks and I will find my way from there. All I will need from you is a place to lay my head during that time . . ."

An act of sheer bravado, or blatant stupidity, I now believed, for I had worked out that my six hundred and fifty pounds would run out during week four – I'd go belly up . . . broke.

My one hope: that I might find Rodney, who would perhaps be more accommodating.

My thoughts vaporised as the captain's disembodied voice announced we had just passed over the tip of England, at Land's End. The aircraft had started its descent to Heathrow.

Other worries assailed me. Would Rosemary have received my letter? If so, how did she react? And crucially – would there be anyone at the airport to meet me?

CHAPTER 10

Speedbird 0071 swept across southern England, descended over Southampton, and banked east before making the final turns to land at London's Heathrow Airport.

From my seat in the centre row, I could see little, but making a final trip to the toilet I peered out the window at the landscape below. Wispy grey clouds scudded by over a green patchwork of fields miles below; a far cry from the concrete jungle I'd come to expect of an English landscape.

"Home sweet home," the old lady smiled up at me as I sat back down. "You'll have to get used to the cold, dear."

I smiled sheepishly, feeling an ominous chill run down my spine.

Not before long, the seat belt signs flashed on. The flight attendants retired to their well-secured positions. I felt that now-familiar dread welling up inside me. A sudden deep rumble caused me to stiffen in my seat.

"Don't worry, dear," squeaked my petite companion, placing a wrinkled hand on my forearm, "This is just the landing gear being lowered."

More hydraulic-type noises could be heard as the flaps were extended incrementally – each sound adding to my trepidation – as the plane rocketed toward *terra firma* at two hundred miles an hour.

"This is the best bit," my elderly companion grinned, revealing those snow-white dentures, perhaps also revealing something of the woman she once had been. Apparently seeing the look of terror etched on my face, she patted my hand. "It'll be fine; these people do this all the time."

I nodded, the rest of my body paralysed with fear.

Then, for some unfathomable reason, my mind chose to remind me of a particular chilling reality. It chose this very instant to remind me that the landing was one of the most treacherous aspects of air travel.

Oh my God!

My arms shook slightly from the force of gripping the armrest with all my might. My lips were moving in silent prayer.

Heart-stopping, body-stiffening minutes later, miraculously, and with barely a jolt, the colossal machine was roaring down the runway of the world's busiest airport, slowing from its touchdown speed of 183 miles an hour. Outside the window, grey concrete structures tore by in a blur. I felt a wave of euphoric relief sweeping through me as I leaned back in my seat, heaved a huge sigh of relief, shut my eyes, crossed myself twice, and thanked the Almighty for great mercies.

As the aircraft turned to taxi to a stop, a mono-lithic, grey concrete structure loomed outside the windows – the terminal building, I imagined. Another wave of euphoria swept through my bones for at no point during the cross-Atlantic trek had I been convinced that Speedbird 0071 hadn't been destined to become a blot on British Airways' exemplary safety record.

Smiling inwardly, I marvelled, recalling that only eight hours before I had stood petrified, staring up at the huge contraption, my logical mind having great difficulty comprehending how a lift-off could be possible, and even greater difficulty accepting that the aircraft really would, travelling at almost the speed of sound ten miles up in the sky, cross the ocean, and then touch down at a predetermined point some four thousand miles away.

"White Man's magic," I chuckled.

My petite companion, now sporting an even brighter shade of red lipstick, and smelling like a bottle of Anais Anais, smiled and nodded at me as I helped her up as soon as the seat belt sign pinged off.

My carry-on bag hung from my shoulder as I sheep-ishly followed the multitudes laden with bags and parcels, making their way briskly through the chilly terminal building, heading towards Immigration. I soon felt lost, perplexed. Something was terribly amiss. For the life of me, I could not remember leaving the aircraft. I recalled no walk down the steep metal stairs onto the tarmac; no walk across the tarmac to the terminal building. In fact, the last thing I remembered was ambling down the aisle at the back of an almost stagnant queue. The next thing I knew, I was walking through a cold building – the terminal building.

How come?

Perplexed, I quickly put the matter to rest, concluding that I might have suffered a temporary bout of amnesia, not altogether something to be unduly worried about. In my quest for knowledge, I hadn't yet come across the 'jetway' – a movable bridge that allowed passengers to exit the aircraft onto a covered walkway that led them, sheltered from the elements, directly into the terminal building.

I arrived at the immigration desk, feeling the chilled air seeping through my lightweight leatherette jacket. In the queue to my right I spotted the little old man in the ill-fitting three-piece suit and sagging red bow-tie. He looked decidedly ten years younger, and seemed to have got rid of that incessant blink.

I fought off a shaky sensation in my legs as I approached the immigration desk. It surprised me that, far from being a uniformed "officer", the man behind the desk looked like a businessman in a two-piece suit. Like most passing through UK immigration, I didn't realize then, that, far from being mere functionaries, immigration officers were highly-trained plain-clothes detectives trained to sniff out criminals, drug traffickers and the like.

My passport and landing card inspected, the officer proceeded to ask, almost casually, how long I intended to stay, did I have a place to stay, did I have sufficient funds, where would I be studying. All quite politely conversational, I thought. My answers seemed to do the trick, for, with a satisfied smile, the official stamped my passport and handed it back, wishing me a pleasant stay and success in my accountancy studies.

I had earlier noted that one or two passengers ahead of me had been directed to another officer who led them to a small glass-walled side office, presumably for further questioning, perhaps destined for the next flight home. I counted my blessings, and, for the hundredth time, thanked the merciful God.

Mopping the beads of cold sweat from my brow, I entered the United Kingdom.

Now, where is my luggage?

Above the multitude of heads bobbing up and down in Arrivals, my eyes scanned the surroundings for signs pointing the way to the baggage-collection area. No luck. I decided to follow the crowd, and finally found the carousel trundling around and around with the baggage from my flight.

I saw that the more seasoned travellers had suitcases with built-in wheels; others had managed to find trolleys from somewhere. Perhaps noticing how much I was struggling under the weight of my two large suitcases, a pleasant-faced man in a two-piece suit directed me to an alcove to the far right, where I retrieved a trolley from a stack, and loaded up my cases.

But I soon realised that baggage trolleys tend to be a bit like beasts of burden, inasmuch as they seem to have a mind of their own. My navigational efforts produced a highly erratic path towards and through the 'Nothing to Declare' channel.

As I pulled the trolley to a stop at the exit, a viciously cold gust that seemed to tear through my body chilled me instantly to the bone. I felt shivers rippling through me as I gasped at what seemed the entire population of London waiting in the freezing cold, clad in full winter gear that had me feeling stark naked. Some stood in clusters behind a barrier, holding up placards bearing the names of individuals I didn't recognize. I spotted small pockets of black people, their expressions betraying their anxiety, some casting quick glances at me, looking away just as quickly.

My pulse fluttered as my weary eyes scanned the sea of faces. *Perhaps Rosemary hadn't received my letter? Perhaps she hadn't an inkling that I'd decided to defy her wishes not to come to the UK?*

I stood in the freezing air, feeling an awful premonition of dread.

Damn! What the hell do I do now?

I felt surging exasperation, the beginnings of loneliness, the terrible trepidation of finding myself lost in a gigantic deep freeze, thousands of miles from home. Torrents of panicky thoughts began to cascade through my mind, each worse than the other, adding to my already deepening gloom.

Then my panic-stricken eyes spied, standing amid the searching crowd, a tall, dark young man, smiling cheerfully, seemingly at me.

My heart leaped in joy for I recognized him instantly. Simon looked much as he did in the photos Rosemary had sent from England. With slitted eyes under full, almost epicanthal folds, much the same as mine, and roughly my height, my half-brother was a couple years younger, several shades darker, and certainly much more appropriately dressed, than me. Clad in a slick black leather jacket, and in those loose-fitting jeans, I could tell instantly that he was comfortably warm and very much in fashion – much more than I could say of myself.

Our faces spread into broad grins as we greeted each other with firm handshakes and a brief embrace. I felt a surge of relief cascading through me, delighted that my family hadn't forsaken me, after all.

My eyes searched around expectantly for my mother and three sisters. "Where is everyone?"

"Just me, mate" Simon replied, his English accent strong, his voice deep, with a cheerful smile.

I tried to conceal my utter surprise that an entourage of family members, as there would have been in the Caribbean, hadn't been waiting to greet me with wide open arms. My astonishment soon faded when I began to count my blessings; blessings that the plane hadn't crashed, and that I wouldn't get lost trudging through the airport with my heavy load, all alone.

Then another surprise hit me.

"Come on mate," said the English accent, "Let's get going. We've a ways to go. Let me have the money and I'll get the train tickets."

I was silently astounded that, far from being greeted like a king, I now had to pay for my and my brother's journey back from the airport. I fished in my wallet and handed Simon a crisp ten-pound note.

Things are done rather differently over here.

I followed my brother, now burdened with one of my suitcases. We plunged through the crowds and, less than ten minutes later, were standing on the busy platform of Heathrow underground station. A warm, dry, stuffy wind rushed through the tunnel, followed by a low rumble that grew louder and louder. As the train roared into the station, screeching to a halt on the platform before us, my looks of utter amazement delivered an amused smile to Simon's face.

"You know, mate," he said, smiling roguishly, his eyes glinting with amusement, "These trains run all under London – and lots of them go under the River Thames as well."

125

My jaw dropped, then I heaved a huge sigh of relief when my brother declared that this portion of our journey excluded a submarine excursion beneath the world-famous waterway. I'd had quite enough new experiences for one day.

The train rattled us along underground, and twenty bewildering minutes later we were swept out of the carriage in a tide of incurious commuters. Up the escalator we went, through the ticket barrier, and we emerged from our subterranean trek into the daylight and relatively fresh air of Euston Station. For the first time, I got a brief glimpse of the frenetic life that was London. The station itself, Simon explained, was a new construction that had replaced the architecture of the Victorian original. Awestruck by the grandeur of the edifice, I realised that St. Lucia's entire population of one hundred and fifty thousand could comfortably fit into this enormous space. With shops selling everything from books and magazines to ties and stockings, the station resembled a glass-enclosed city.

I gazed curiously at the chaos of people hurrying along this way and that, clasping paper cups, half-eaten sandwiches, and newspapers. Many were besuited and carrying briefcases. I understood not a word of the strange, disembodied nasal voice blaring out from the PA system, though people about me seemed to change direction immediately at its command.

Others stood gazing up at the enormous departure board overhead, its black and white tabs shuffling and reshuffling downwards as the information refreshed. Simon didn't have to look up to determine the scheduled departure time for the next train to Milton Keynes Central – he knew the drill.

He guided me to the ticket window. I forked out the thirty pounds to pay for the two second-class tickets. Minutes later we bustled our way on to the British Rail train that sat idling on Platform Five, preparing for departure.

Much to my relief, the train had no delusions about being an earthworm; Simon assured me it would remain above ground for the entire journey to Milton Keynes, some fifty miles northwards.

A warning whistle sounded, and the packed train lurched out of Euston station. It felt safe – much safer than air travel. I craned my neck looking for the nearest exit. *Good. If anything, I can always bail out through that window.*

As the train trundled through the environs of the city, without a glimmer of sunlight breaking through the dark cloud cover, I found the soot-stained brick buildings whizzing by outside surprisingly drab and dreary. Soon we were speeding out into open country, and the buildings got few and farther between. Along the way, the train stopped at stations with, it seemed to me, bizarre names like Leighton Buzzard and Hemel Hempstead, which somehow conjured up memories of a character from one of my primary school books – Rumpelstiltskin. The journey took us past medieval-looking brick buildings with chimneys, calling to mind the story of the 'Three Little Pigs' which fascinated me as a child. Expansive snow-blanketed fields dominated the landscape whizzing by outside.

Nothing like the concrete jungle my friends had told me to expect.

As the British Rail locomotive sped towards Milton Keynes, Simon and I chatted about this and that, but mainly, to satisfy our mutual curiosity, asked and fielded questions about each other: our family, our childhood, our school days, our mother

I soon discovered that it was only the day before that Simon had learned I'd be boarding a plane to England. Sheila had telegrammed Rosemary, which was just as well because our mother hadn't the slightest inkling that I'd decided to defy her order to stay at home. Evidently, Rosemary hadn't received my hastily written, defiant letter. But I was grateful nonetheless, that with the news Sheila had delivered, Rosemary had dispatched my kindly brother to the airport to meet me.

I had taken a risk; it paid off. Had I not taken the plunge, I would perhaps never again have had the opportunity to set foot on British soil. As I listened to Simon's voice, I kept revelling, at the back of my mind, in the reality that finally I had reached the UK, a giant step towards fulfilling my dream.

I'll deal with consequences later. Nothing can stop me now. I'm here, in the UK – that's all that matters!

As we neared our destination, more patchy snow

littered the ground, seeming to get thicker and thicker the closer and closer we got. The train began to slow down. I heard a racket up and down the carriage; people seemed to be scrambling to the door, ready to get off.

When we alighted at Milton Keynes Central station, I marvelled that everywhere seemed blanketed in white – but not the fluffy, cotton-wool, snowball-making-type snow I had seen on television. Instead it was cold, wet, and slushy and, where traffic had driven through it, it had become a dirty, sloppy, brown mush embedded with grit.

As we moved into the open, I was rapidly engulfed in bitter cold. The temperature quickly proved too severe for my leatherette jacket; sections of the black coating had already peeled off, revealing a light blue undercoating. I breathed relief when Simon suggested we hail a taxi rather than await the bus. For a change, I didn't mind the added expense. My sweater and corduroys that had been stiflingly hot at home seemed no match for the wintry climate.

The taxi sped through the streets of Milton Keynes, lurching round roundabout after roundabout. Despite jet lag and exhaustion, I peered determinedly through the frosted windows out onto streets that were oddly darkened in mid-afternoon. Futuristic-looking rectangular structures of glass and steel rose in the distance and fell away as we sped by. Skeletal trees lined the boulevards we drove through – these trees, devoid of leaves and, seemingly, life, tore by in a blur.

Simon explained that Milton Keynes, a relatively new town, was built to house the overflow from London, offering more reasonably priced homes and business properties than available in the nation's capital.

It was ten anxious minutes later that the cab found its way to Speedwell Place, an anonymous-looking street of yellow-brick buildings. I felt slightly disoriented, finding it difficult to differentiate one building from the other, being used, as I was, to the colourful paint schemes and varying designs of the detached houses that characterised residential construction in the Caribbean. The yellow structures, however, seemed redeemed by their newness, unlike many of the centuries-old, medieval-looking buildings I had seen along the way.

"Council flats," offered Simon, eagerly. "You just put your name down on the list and when one comes vacant, in you go. Cheap, too – the rent's nothing, and if you can't pay then, the council pays it for you. They come and paint 'em and everything. It's brilliant!"

Before leaving the relative warmth of the car, I dug into my pocket yet again, and paid the cab driver ten pounds, mentally noting that within the few hours of arriving on British soil, I had already spent sixty pounds – ten pounds an hour – one tenth of my total wealth.

Under depressing grey skies, the icy wind buffeted my jacket, chilling me to the bone.

Everything felt frozen: my ears, my face, my hands, my feet.

In silent apprehension, struggling under the weight of my luggage, we plodded up to the door of no. 210 Speedwell Place.

The fear of the flight, the newness of my surroundings, the cold, the trains, and even the snow, momentarily fell away from my mind.

I could not believe this was actually happening. Finally, I was here . . . right here on my mother's doorstep . . . on Rosemary's doorstep!

I screwed up my face against the rush of icy wind, and at the same time pinched my arm, exchanging a nervous grin with my brother.

His hand reached out slowly towards the little white button up on the wall next to the door.

He pressed it.

The doorbell rang.

CHAPTER 11

With my jacket collar turned up against the wind, a wave of apprehension washed over me as I wrung my blue-chilled hands, shifting my weight nervously from foot to foot. I felt the bitter cold penetrating to the bone, uncontrollable chills raking my flesh. Not knowing what to expect, my heart fluttered as my eyes riveted to the blue wooden door of 210 Speedwell Place.

All my life I'd imagined this moment – finally meeting my mother, seeing her face for the first time. Now, at twenty-two, standing here . . . on Rosemary's doorstep, shoulder to shoulder with my half-brother, it seemed surreal. Somehow, I half expected to awaken abruptly in my bed, back home in St. Lucia. My mind fled back to the letter I'd so hurriedly written, and in that fleeting instant I wished desperately that I was, in fact, dreaming. At the eleventh hour – after I'd made all my plans, after I'd resigned my job, after I'd bought my ticket – devastating news had suddenly arrived from

Rosemary. No longer was she willing or able to accommodate me; I should remain in St. Lucia . . . cancel my plans. Unthinkable. Crazy.

Feeling like an accused awaiting his fate, terrible doubts assailed me. Had I reacted too hastily? Had I made commitments I couldn't live up to? The compromise I'd suggested weighed heavily on my mind. Three weeks; that was all the time I'd given myself to vacate my mother's house. With my funds already rapidly depleting, it seemed I'd set myself a daunting task.

My one glimmer of hope lay in tracking down my elusive father, something which I prayed Rosemary would be able to help me with. The thought of trekking four thousand miles and not seeking him out – wherever he might be hiding – seemed to me as insane a thought as abandoning my plans to travel to England altogether.

Stamping my feet on the frosted concrete, feeling the dull, prickly sensation shooting up my legs, I blew briskly into my bare hands, hoping the hint of warmth in my breath would bring some little comfort to fingers that had already lost all sensation. I could do nothing, however, to sooth my aching, half-frozen ears.

Still no sign of life from within. Simon's knuckles rapped the door, perhaps a little too aggressively. He glanced over at me and shrugged as if to say, 'I haven't a clue what's going on inside there, mate."

I smiled as the distant sounds of cheerful children drew my attention. I turned, peered at a throng of four, maybe five, infants in colourful all-in-one hooded thermal suits playing under street lamps, running here and there, their screams of delight echoing in the snowy landscape. Atop a nearby hill that ran alongside a steep flight of frost-covered stairs, three little boys piled into a red sleigh, hurtling down the slippery slope, screaming with delight as they crashed into the snow-filled bank.

Despite the numbing chill I was enduring, I felt a rush of warmth, my face spreading into a broad smile as my mind wheeled back to my childhood fantasies – frolicking in the snow, building snowmen, pelting snowballs at my sister. Fantasies that were not to be.

"Al'right?" Simon nodded politely to a smiling black couple dressed up like Eskimos as they ambled by, pushing a pram on the pavement on the far side of the road. My teeth chattering, I found myself wondering how much it would dent my finances were I to acquire similar attire to insulate my slim body from this brutal cold. Just then a viciously chilled wind lashed my already numb face. I grimaced, wondering how on earth I'd ever survive these arctic conditions.

Then I heard it.

The door catch. It clicked.

My pulse quickened.

A mischievous smile crossed Simon's face when our glistening eyes met. An expectant smile pulled at my quivering lips.

The moment had finally arrived.

Slowly, the door began to open . . . slowly.

I waited, holding my breath.

Then I saw, appearing in the doorway, slowly, an arm, a shoulder, a face . . . an almost oriental face . . . a pale almost oriental face beaming up at me, bashfully.

A wobbly smile quavering on my face, my heart fluttering, I blinked, studying the face – the light complexion, the high cheekbones, the almond-shaped eyes all but hidden beneath fleshy eye-folds. Yes. It was her. It was a mature version of the indi-vidual whose picture, for as long as I can remember, adorned our living room wall back home. Yes . . . it was Rosemary . . . my mother . . . clad in a blue cardigan over a long, thick grey dress.

My heart was still fluttering when she spoke.

"Hi, Rudy." Her voice, soft and gentle with a slight inflection, sounded exactly as it had that fateful day when, out of the blue, she had called.

For a moment I stood there, in the doorway, motionless, my smile hovering, adrenalin coursing through me, the reality of the situation striking me. Here, in England, in Milton Keynes, in the cold, I stood face to face with the woman who had given birth to me – a meeting that was an everyday occur-rence for most, but a novelty for me.

Yet, oddly, despite my simmering nerves, despite my adrenalin rush, despite my galloping heart, I felt no upwelling of emotion; no sudden urge to take this woman in my arms in a Hollywood-style mother-and-son reunion. Rather, what I felt was more akin to meeting, finally, a long-lost distant relative; a pleasurable event, an exciting event, but an event devoid of bells, devoid of whistles, devoid of a philharmonic orchestra symphonizing in the background.

With Rosemary, the woman before me, my mother, I felt no kinship.

"Hi . . . there," I replied, hesitating, smiling, unsure what to call her, but knowing that 'Mummy' wasn't on the cards.

Our embrace was brief, and strange, and awkward.

Simon pushed me gently from behind. "Come on, mate, it's freezing out here!"

I smiled as he struggled under the weight of the two suitcases.

After the freezing hell outside, I welcomed the redeeming warmth of the medium-sized, modestly furnished room into which Rosemary ushered me. My eyes immediately fell upon three young girls crammed together on a fluffy brown sofa, grinning expectantly.

There could be no mistaking those eyes, those almond-shaped eyes. We were family.

I strode towards them. They rose to greet me.

"Hello, I'm Deneice . . . your sister," the dark-skinned one chirped in her English accent, the cheeks of her attractive round face dimpling as she smiled up at me with those eyes, her head barely reaching my chest.

"Hi Deneice, nice to meet you . . . I know who

you are," I said, smiling at the sixteen-year-old clad in thick, brown corduroys and a thick turtle-neck jumper. We exchanged a brief swaying embrace.

A light-complexioned girl, no more than thirteen, and donned in a heavy wool jumper over long black skirt – was the spitting image of her mother . . . our mother.

"Hiya! I'm Natalie, but you can call me Natty," came her lilting voice.

"Hi, Natalie, nice to meet you," I said, pulling her gently into a brief hug.

Rosemary, seemingly rooted to a spot in the centre of the room, hadn't stopped smiling. I felt her glistening eyes boring into me, tracking my every movement, like a proud mother admiring her toddler's first steps.

I turned my attention to the youngest of my sisters, no more than ten or eleven. She hung back, almost hiding in the shadows of her sisters, her gaze riveted on the carpeted floor. The smile I sent her provoked no response. Her slitted eyes remained fixed to the floor, as if studying the patterns in the thick carpet that matched the colourful wool jumper that she wore over a long maroon skirt.

"This is Theresa . . . she's a bit shy," Deneice said, with a hint of apology.

"Take a seat, Rudy; give me your coat," said Rosemary from behind me, as I planted a kiss on Theresa's cheek.

"That's okay; I'll keep it on for now." I needed to preserve what little body-warmth I had left.

The bashful smile lingering at the corners of her mouth, Rosemary then motioned me to a large armchair next to the long sofa. "Do you like tea?"

"Yes, thank you."

My mother disappeared into a room I presumed was the kitchen.

"So we finally meet," I breathed, eyeing my sisters, feeling somewhat at a loss for words, as I settled into the cushy armchair.

"Yeah, it's great, but kinda weird meeting you after all this time," said Deneice.

"Yeah . . . but I'm really happy it has finally happened . . . better late than never," I said.

"Do you like the snow?" Natalie asked, with a mischievous little grin.

Deneice rolled her eyes at her younger sister.

"It's wetter than I thought it would be." I shrugged, smiling at Simon, who sat quietly on an armchair in the corner across the warm room, as though his day's work was done.

Rosemary returned with a large, steaming mug. She set it on the centre table before me, and took a seat on the fluffy brown sofa. That timid smile lingered on her face. I wondered what thoughts were playing in her mind, what emotions she felt. Did I remind her of someone . . . perhaps a young man called Rodney?

I brought the mug up to my lips, and immediately caught myself thinking how weak the English tea seemed compared to the *Red Rose* variety I was used to back home.

Natalie's voice intruded my thoughts, bringing me back. "Nice jumper," she said, barely choking back a giggle, prompting a fierce glare from Simon.

She sent me a melting apologetic smile. I returned a smile that said, 'No problem.'

We continued to exchange pleasantries, searching for words to keep the conversation flowing, jumping from one subject to another in a disjointed, jumbled manner.

As we sat there, it occurred to me that towards my siblings I felt the same emotional void that I felt towards Rosemary . . . the lack of kinship; perhaps just the shock of a first encounter; perhaps in time the void would be filled. I hoped so. But that little voice in my head told me that the bond of a biological mother would do little to bridge the seemingly unbridgeable gap. I couldn't quite put a finger on what exactly this gap represented. But I sensed a gap . . . an indefinable gap . . . a gap on both sides. Perhaps a cultural gap of sorts?

After about twenty awkward minutes, as if running late for a crucial appointment, Deneice's eyes started to dart, with increasing frequency, to her watch. Finally, Rosemary appeared to nod at her daughter, sending Deneice jumping to her feet.

"I'm off" she said, "See ya later Rudy – nice to meet ya." Turning on her heel, she strode off without so much as a backward glance. I would also have said goodbye, if I could have spluttered the words out before she closed the door behind her.

"She shares a flat with her mate around the corner." Simon said, "Nice council flat, too."

Natalie sprang to her feet. "I'm off to see me mates. Nice to meet ya, Rudy." She smiled, leaving the room in a flurry.

"Okay, pleasure meeting you . . . have fun," I called out, uncertain whether my thirteen-year-old sister had heard me.

"Good evening, young man," a booming voice said from behind me.

I turned to see a tall, dark-skinned, heavyset, half-Indian man in his early fifties. Wearing a dark brown three-piece suit, he stood in the doorway of the living room, gazing down at me, a faint smile touching his lips.

"I'm Francis – welcome to our humble dwelling." His strong-toned voice resonated through the room, as he strode towards me, his hand extended.

I rose to shake hands with him, noticing that the man suffered a slight limp, the result of a serious motor vehicle accident a few years back, as I had read in one of Rosemary's letters. Francis, my step-father, held a PhD in economics, and had migrated from Trinidad some forty years before – something else Rosemary's letter had told me.

Francis smiled. "How are you finding our green and pleasant land?" he said, lowering himself awkwardly onto the sofa next to his wife, my mother.

"Cold!" Simon chuckled.

I smiled agreement.

140

Francis shot Simon a ferocious condemning look, a look that could speak so loudly, without words. My brother seemed to shrivel into his shell.

Francis turned towards me, consciously excluding Simon. "I trust your flight was comfortable?"

"Yes." I nodded, "It was certainly an experience, with some dubious moments. But I'm delighted to be here finally. It was well worth it. I've been dreaming about this for as long as I can remember."

Francis arched his bushy brows. "Very good, very good," he said, glancing across to Rosemary; a single nod of his head seemed to suggest approval, and my mother beamed like a schoolgirl who had just been awarded a surprise A grade.

At that moment, it dawned on me that my step-father might have been the author of Rosemary's letters. The man spoke in much the same formal tone as I had noted in those typed letters.

He settled back in his seat, his dark eyes studying me. "I think you will find things a little different in the mother country compared to the West Indies, my dear boy."

Then he took me to school, in a formal, scholarly tone, on what he considered the problems with the British youth.

"Not like back home," he assured me, his eyes flicking a menacing glance at Simon who it seemed, would have preferred to have been elsewhere.

I listened, occasionally smiling, nodding, but infinitely more interested in observing my mother,

her gaze riveted to Francis, as if trying to draw on his strength, her eyes glistening with undisguised adoration for her husband as he delivered his stinging diatribe on black British youth – their lack of respect for elders, their lack of ambition, their lack of this, their lack of that. Occasionally, Rosemary chipped in with little anecdotes praising the way the kids back home conducted themselves in the presence of adults – anecdotes that seemed more than a little foreign to me.

After seemingly satisfying himself that I'd deciphered his coded message – his message that I shouldn't allow myself to be corrupted by my siblings – Francis excused himself. He hoisted his body up from his seat as if the movement required the full strength of both arms to lift his ample frame. Directing a brief nod of farewell to his wife, then to me, but not to Simon, he hobbled out of the room and disappeared up the narrow stairs.

Rosemary's gaze focused on the staircase as if she was already missing her husband.

It stunned me when she let it slip that it had been only two years before they had tied the matrimonial knot. I was equally stunned to hear that it was Francis who had moved into Rosemary's council house, and not the other around. Somehow, I'd assumed that the holder of a PhD in economics would be the provider, and not the beneficiary, of charity.

From his darkened corner, trying to suppress a yawn with the back of his hand, Simon broke his prolonged silence. "You're in with me, mate."

He rose from his seat and grabbed the larger, heavier suitcase. Excusing myself, I rose stiffly, picked up the other suitcase, and followed Simon. I felt Rosemary's gaze on my back as we disappeared up the narrow flight of stairs.

Theresa's eyes remained fixed on the carpeted floor.

CHAPTER 12

I shifted uncomfortably on the single bed, my eyes surveying the little room that was clearly Simon's haven. In a corner, a wooden table sagged under the weight of music-industry magazines, LP records and two turntables. A pile of clothes, pushed haphazardly to one corner, made way for my suitcases.

"So what do you think of your Mom?" asked Simon, sitting on the comfortably shabby armchair in his room in the attic, after a light meal.

"Who?"

"Mom . . . our mother."

"Oh!" I said, somewhat embarrassed that I hadn't associated the word 'Mom' with Rosemary.

"She seems a bit quiet . . . almost shy, and it's clear that she adores Francis."

Simon's deep, accented voice came through, dismissive, indignant. "Her and Francis are as thick as thieves. You never stand a chance against them."

"How come?"

"They never disagree, ever." Simon folded his

arms, his brow furrowing. "Every minute of the day they always find something to criticise us for. It's a nightmare. They just sit there shaking their heads as if we were the biggest disappointments in the world!"

"They never disagree?"

"Well it's more like Mom never disagrees with him."

Simon fell silent for several long moments, lost in his thoughts, his forehead creased.

"What's St Lucia like?" he asked suddenly, as though the thought had instantly popped into his head.

"Warm, and full of colour."

Simon curled up in the armchair that had become his bed since my arrival, as I sold him my island paradise. I told him of St. Lucia's location in the Caribbean Sea; the year-round sunny weather; the warmth of the people; this girl called Susanna who I intended to marry some day. By the time I had finished, it had occurred to me for the first time just how much I loved my country, how much I'd taken it for granted, and how much I'd surely miss it over the next few years.

"Sounds great . . . I hope to visit there some day."

Looking at me searchingly, he then added, "So why did you want to come over here?"

"I'm on a mission; my dream is to be an accountant. I expect to get qualified and return home to a big job. That's my life-long dream, man."

Steve frowned, as if perplexed. "What, you've had that dream ever since you were a kid?"

"Pretty much."

"Wow, that's great, mate . . . I'm sure you'll pass with flying colours."

"What about you . . . what did you dream about when you were a kid?"

"To tell the truth, mate, when I was little, the only thing I ever dreamed about was having a cupboard jam-packed with all sorts of goodies – you know, like biscuits, and chocolates . . . all sorts of snacks."

My eyebrows arched in surprise.

"We were always hungry when we were kids," Simon continued, his head bowed slightly. "Sometimes we would be left home alone for hours at a time with empty cupboards and nothing to eat while our mom was out working. All I could dream about then was when I grew up I would see to it that my cupboards were always packed with lots of stuff to eat, so that I would never have to go hungry again."

His tone was muted as he relayed stories of his childhood; stories that weighed down my heart, too.

When he fell into a pensive silence, and with the image of my youngest sister hiding behind Natalie still fresh in my mind, I asked, "So, what's the story with Theresa? Why's she so shy?"

After a moment's hesitation, Simon spoke, his tone suddenly bitter. "That was our neighbour."

"Your neighbour?

Glaring at the bare wooden floor, his eyes unfocused, his voice subdued, he said, "Most nights

146

when we were home alone this woman, one of Mom's friends – a neighbour – used to pop in from time to time. She was the ugliest white woman I'd ever seen . . . a real hag!"

I chuckled.

"Anyway, one night we're all at home alone, alone in the dark, and this woman walks in. Theresa was a toddler fast asleep in her crib."

Simon paused, his face heavy with anger, or regret, or both.

"For no reason whatsoever," he continued, "the bloody witch just grabs my baby sister's wrists and bends them."

My head jerked back as if I had just been slapped.

"Theresa's screaming her head off, and this woman just goes on hurting her."

My eyes were open as wide as my mouth.

Simon swallowed hard before continuing. "The old cow broke both of Theresa's wrists. Since then my little sister has been scared of her own shadow."

I blinked, and blinked again. "That's crazy."

"I saw it all, mate. I hid under the table in the dark, too scared to help my baby sister. For as long as I live, I'll never ever forget that night. My little sister's life has been destroyed . . . she will never recover from this. I didn't help her . . . I . . ."

His voice shuddered and broke.

I shook my head, slowly, ruefully, swallowing hard against the unfamiliar aching lump in my throat. For several long minutes, I could only stare at my brother whose eyes hadn't left the floor.

147

Slowly, though, my stunned expression faded and became more thoughtful. My mind took me right back to the summer of 1972 when Sheila had disappeared to the UK for three and a half weeks – twenty-five dismal days that I marked off each morning on a calendar on my bedroom wall. And now, for the first time, it dawned upon me why my aunt, after she'd returned home, had suddenly got cold on the idea of sending Roslyn and me to live with our mother.

The next evening, lounging in the living room after sitting through an episode of *EastEnders*, and after Francis had hobbled up to his room, I quizzed Rosemary about Rodney. Did she know how to reach him? Did she know his last address, or telephone number? Did she know where he worked, or what he did for a living? Did she know anything at all?

Doubt wrinkled her forehead into a thoughtful knot. Then she spoke. She hadn't the slightest inkling of how to trace the father of her two eldest children. She recalled that he'd lived in Surrey, the other side of London, the last she knew. I listened intently to my mother who, with slightly downcast eyes, told her story, her voice at times, weak, faltering.

I was a year and three months when Rosemary had left St. Lucia for London, in search of her fiancé. Unable to find him, she had moved in with her older brother who had been resident in the UK for many years. When finally she tracked down Rodney, she had received the shock of her life. She rang his door-bell. A dark-skinned woman with a Barbadian accent and a very swollen abdomen greeted her. The pregnant woman invited Rosemary into the apartment. A red-faced Rodney met his childhood sweetheart in the living room, glancing nervously at the pregnant woman as she disappeared reluctantly into an adjacent room. Rodney, seemingly stricken with guilt, admitted that the lady carrying his baby had recently become his wife. Rosemary said nothing of what happened next. The childhood sweethearts, although avowed to a life together, went their separate ways. Rosemary had last glimpsed my father more than eighteen years ago . . . behind the wheel of a big, red, double-decker London bus.

My misty eyes studied Rosemary both in sorrow and in stunned disbelief. She'd had a dreadful experience, and it showed in her eyes. I shared her pain, I shared her sorrow; pain and sorrow from which it seemed she hadn't yet recovered . . . not after twenty-two years. But all the same, I knew instinctively what this spelled for me. It spelled Trouble; I now had no Plan C.

How on earth will I be able to get in touch with the man?

"My God, Rudy, you look so much like Rodney when you look at me that way!" She exclaimed, her eyes opening wide. "You're the picture of your father, and you have the same mannerisms, too!"

For a long moment she just sat there, fixated on me, as if in some trance.

Then she smiled. "He was a fabulous table-tennis player, you know."

Over the next half-hour I listened to my mother, whose eyes and mood had regained some levity, as she told of how Rodney became a champion table-tennis player in Barbados. How he became a local celebrity, his picture regularly appearing in local newspapers.

Then, with her eyes once again finding the floor, Rosemary declared in a more sombre tone that life had been difficult for her. Coming to the UK had been no bed of roses. After all, she had been only nineteen. Her hopes, her dreams, her aspirations, had all come crashing down around her. And Rodney . . .

She changed the topic.

It wasn't long before it dawned on me that my presence in the household had stirred up a certain amount of friction, unsettling further an already unsettled environment. In my presence, Francis openly chastised my siblings, demanding that they behave more like me, extolling the virtues of Caribbean youth; British youngsters were rude, unruly and uncaring by comparison. The couple seemed convinced that the islands had remained much as they had left them, decades ago. They were woefully out of touch.

All to no avail, I tried explaining that over the years West Indian children had found their voices and were no longer timid and afraid to speak up in the presence of adults. The kids no longer believed in 'being seen and not heard,' the practice of days gone by.

Ill at ease with the brewing friction, I reminded myself time and again not to get caught up in family politics and that I should never lose sight of my goal to study, pass exams, and return home to the job that I knew, in my hearts of hearts, awaited me.

Of my three sisters, it was Deneice who offered the biggest challenge to me. I couldn't help observing how increasingly sullen she appeared in my presence, unable to hide what seemed some sort of resentment . . . resentment of me. *Why?*

"It's because we were told that you and Roslyn looked down on us," Simon explained in a matter-of-fact sort of way during one of our many late night talks. "We were told that you and Roslyn looked down on us because we were so black."

"Who said that?" I asked, indignant.

"We were just told that you were ashamed of us, and that you called our dad an ugly black man, with a nose so large and flat that when he cried the tears rolled from one side of his face across to the other."

I bristled at the allegation. "That's nonsense, man!"

Simon shrugged, looking like a wounded pup.

Then, without warning, without prior agreement, with us apparently no longer able to suppress the overwhelming sensation welling up in our chests, our shoulders began to shake . . . they began to

151

move up and down uncontrollably, and the next thing we knew, irrepressible laughter was belting out from our throats, gusty shouts of laughter ringing out through the small room, until we could take it no more, and began to cough and choke, tears streaming down our cheeks.

The following morning I was not laughing when Rosemary brought up the inevitable.

"I received your letter," she murmured hesitantly, looking up at me, a telltale flush turning her pale cheeks a bright red.

She looked away, embarrassed. "It wasn't my idea . . . it . . . it was . . ." she hesitated, then decided silence was best.

"Do you want to talk about it now?" I asked.

"No . . . no . . . not now."

Neither did I laugh when, the next day, sitting in the living room, and after a long awkward silence, Rosemary turned to me. "Things are difficult for me, Rudy," she started. "Francis has never worked since his accident; all his compensation money has finished . . . and we're all on the dole."

I found the word 'dole' a strange name for the British social security system that made monthly payments to unemployed citizens.

Perhaps I should have been prepared for the words that followed, but I wasn't.

"From now on, Rudy . . . you will have to start paying rent."

CHAPTER 13

Suitcases weighing me down, I cautiously descended the creaky wooden stairs that had known neither paint nor carpet. I would soon discover the room that awaited me in the basement of this squalid Victorian mansion in Paddington, West London.

Paying rent to my mother in Milton Keynes, and then paying on top of that the daily train fare to London Euston from where I then took a long bus ride to college in Greenwich, all added up to no economic sense.

Countless frustrating hours in freezing phone booths dialling dozens of listings under R. Greenidge had proved fruitless. So had my letters to Inland Revenue, and the Department of Health and Social Security, departments that I thought kept a database of UK citizens.

Rodney Greenidge was nowhere to be found.

But when I got in touch with my mother's older brother things began to look up. During the two weeks that I spent with my uncle and his wife at their West London home, my hopes had soared, only to come crashing down the third week. Unlike in the Caribbean, it appeared that in England putting up relatives wasn't the done thing. My uncle had been kind enough, though, to refer me to an old St. Lucian friend with a spare room at his Paddington home.

I creaked down the wooden stairs on the heels of my would-be landlord, my face a mask of stark disappointment, my despair deepening with every step. Whether my decision to come to the UK had been one big mistake or not, was at this point up for grabs.

On the dingy basement landing, I found myself having to manoeuvre my way cautiously through stacks of dusty, disassembled television sets, radios and other broken electrical appliances strewn across the floor that was covered with grime. More than once, I scraped against a smutty wall with layers of peeling, faded wallpaper, soiling my only jacket. I could smell damp, dust, and a stifling odour of gas that instantly constricted my nostrils, giving me a dizzy sensation.

When my uncle had earlier declared that the landlord had 'strange powers' I'd passed it off as a joke, until I saw what happened next.

"Watch that," I heard the tall, lanky, dark-skinned old man say, as he came to a halt in front of a large door half-way down the long, gloomy hallway.

His eyes fixed on some exposed electrical wires in an uncovered wall socket, he added, quickly, "Just don't touch me."

I stood back.

A devilish smile formed at the corners of his mouth, as he reached across and grabbed the exposed wires. Bright blue sparks flew off the coarse fingers.

I boggled, watching the old man electrocuting himself, but strangely, that smile lingered on his face. I smelled burning flesh.

"Just don't touch me!" he cautioned again.

His widening smile declared him unharmed.

"How on earth do you do that?" I asked, astounded.

"I have special powers, man. I can't get shocked," he responded, a hint of arrogance in his voice.

He released the smoking wires and opened his hands for my inspection. I could see black marks where the wires had been in contact with his coarse skin. An eerie feeling crept through my bones as I stared at the old man in his long, black overcoat with its upturned collar. Feeling an ominous tingle in my spine, I wondered whether my uncle knew this man at all.

When I followed him into the gloomy, high-ceilinged room at the end of the dingy basement corridor, no longer did I wonder whether coming to England had been a mistake or not. With stark certainty I knew that it was . . . one terrible mistake.

I was horrified by the dingy room with its single bare light bulb, one small table in a corner, one dilapidated wooden chair, and one enormous bed. The only source of natural light came from a small rectangular window set high in the wall through which I could see the snow-covered ground above. Thick frost had settled on both sides of the window.

I felt an awful sinking feeling in the pit of my stomach, as I found myself thinking it was only a matter of time before I succumbed to the stifling gas fumes that hung heavy in the frigid room. The culprit, the property-owner pointed out, was a leaking gas heater set in the wall. I also soon learned that the wretched heater demanded fifty pence in return for half an hour's heat.

I sighed, realizing this would be my home, my new home . . . it was all I could afford; it would have to do.

I shook the old man's hand, a hand that felt like sandpaper. Grinning, he pocketed the two crisp, twenty-pound notes I'd given him. A week's deposit; a week's rent in advance.

Despite the bitter chill that seemed to permeate my very marrow, there was no way I would give up my fifty pence half-hourly to the leaking gas heater my landlord said he'd soon fix.

It wasn't long before I learned that my problems went beyond bodily warmth.

When the landlord assured me that the slight problem with the plumbing would soon be 'sorted', it hadn't struck me that the entire dilapidated mansion was without running water. Not a drop to wash, to bathe, to flush. Not a single drop.

I wondered how the landlord, his wife, teenage son and daughter got by.

*　　　*　　　*

Every night, after my dinner of a cold, soggy sandwich and canned orange juice from the college canteen, I retired to bed fully clothed – jacket, scarf, boots, the works. In my pitch-dark room, I shivered uncontrollably on my king-sized bed beneath a thick blanket that felt damp to the touch, and was rancid to the smell.

Chilled, stiff, congested, and with a throbbing headache, I rose every day at six, and endured the ninety-minute, three-bus commute to college, where I used the washroom to clean myself and brush my teeth. The curious stares from fellow students I tolerated. For once, pride and dignity were relegated to the back seat.

I thought it could get no worse. But then, on my fifth day, I again complained to my landlord about the broken plumbing.

"Don't worry, man" said the lanky old bloke. Despite some thirty unbroken years in the cold, his rural St. Lucian accent lingered. "The plumbing go be fixed soon. A strong young West Indian boy like you don't need to worry, man. You could bear de little in . . . in . . . con . . . convenience for now."

"I hear you, but I'm not used to living like this. I feel filthy, dirty. I don't mind paying the twenty pounds a week, but I need to have basic facilities . . ."

"Look here man!" the landlord's voice cut through bitterly, "de tenant before you never complained like dis!

"I just trying to help you out," he continued, his

voice sagging with indignation. "Just doing your uncle a favour. You black people complain too damn much! You have it good compared to us when we lot arrived here in de fifties. You all don't know what we went through with all dis racism and ting and paraffin lamps smoking up de blasted rooms. So stop your damn complaining. The Irish lady never complained, and her rent was higher than yours."

"So why did she leave, then?" I probed, defiant.

"She did not leave . . . she die."

"What?"

"Yeah, for two whole days we don't hear de woman. We knock on she door but no answer. We break down de door and find her body stiff on de bed."

My heart skipped a beat. "Which bed?"

"Your bed, man . . ." He gestured towards my bed. "Dat bed."

I felt a chill of fear move down my spine. "What!"

"The poor woman die from pneumonia right here in dis room, on dat bed."

I felt the blood drain from my face as though I'd just seen a ghost.

In a defensive tone, as if he'd suddenly caught himself saying something that perhaps he shouldn't have, the old man fairly shouted, "Listen, man . . . she come here with the sickness . . . not here she catch it . . . !"

Lying in bed that night, terror strafed my soul. I was uncertain which was worse: the obvious threat of contracting pneumonia in this cold, damp room, or the thought of lying on a bed that had once borne a corpse – a rotting, stinking corpse. At the back of my mind, though, I knew my mortal fear had something to do with the pitch darkness of the room, the fear of the supernatural, ghosts, evil spirits, and the like. I hadn't completely got over my fear of the dark, and lurking in the dark recesses of my mind was the thought that somewhere in this house roamed the spirit of some dead Irishwoman.

Not having slept a wink that night, with the first faint ray of sunlight streaming down through the window, I climbed out of bed and, already fully dressed, stalked stiffly in the bitter cold to the newsagents in Paddington High Street. Scouring the papers, I scanned the Classified Ads section for rooms to let.

I hadn't the slightest clue how I'd be able to afford it, but I desperately needed to get out of this godforsaken place.

The third apartment I looked at later that day, in a high-rise building in Deptford, South East London, belonged to an anaemic-looking but otherwise attractive petite woman, not much more than thirty, I imagined. She had pale green eyes and long dark hair pulled into a messy ponytail that seemed terribly at odds with her flowing mint-green evening dress. Claiming to be an out-of-work actress looking to share her apartment, she seemed suitably impressed with my Caribbean heritage. I was more than a little taken aback that she so readily confided in me, her taste for marijuana and, off and on, a sniff of cocaine. The woman spoke so freely on the subject of drugs that I couldn't help but wonder whether she thought all West Indians shared her illicit habit. The spaced-out look in her eyes led me quickly to conclude that her 'occasional use' might well be more of an addiction.

As I got up to leave, promising to get back to her on whether I intended to take up her offer, a black man, early thirties perhaps, with long jet-black dreadlocks flowing from beneath a red, green and yellow knitted hat, strode through the door. The woman's pale green eyes lit up, riveting on to the black plastic bag in the man's hand. I would have uttered 'Goodbye' a second time had I thought she'd have heard my voice.

Something about the man seemed ominous; I wasn't sure if it had anything to do with the way he glared at me as I nodded my way past him, or the strong scent of marijuana emanating from his body.

A little voice in the back of my head whispered to me to keep on searching.

The next day, with my uncle's help, I found myself a room that was clean, affordable, and within a ten-minute bus ride from college.

The landlord, a short, dark-skinned man with a strong Barbadian accent, seemed nice and friendly. The train tracks were perhaps a little close, but nothing unduly bothersome.

This bed-sit, in Lewisham, would be a place I could call home.

CHAPTER 14

And it had all come to this.

Curled up like an unborn child on my small bed, cold, prickly hands clasped between my thighs, I felt stricken . . . stricken with anguish. I couldn't believe my dream, my future, had so abruptly ended. Getting this far, only to be cut down like this, seemed a fate far worse than death. I hadn't bargained for a world of darkness, for a life of total dependency.

What have I done to deserve this?

My eyes were wide open, yet before me I saw nothing but darkness. Like a desert traveller caught up in a swirling sandstorm, I felt lost, hopeless, confused, drained.

I had blown it. My lifelong dream had crashed and burned . . . burned to a crisp.

What am I to do now?

Who should I call? Rosemary, Sheila, my uncle? To what end?

Do I remain in England? To what end?

Do I fly back home? To what end?

161

These thoughts kept echoing bitterly in my head, sinking me deeper and deeper into a morass of despair.

I imagined the talk back home about news of my blindness. The sympathy would be far worse than the ridicule. I could stand neither.

Defeatist thoughts continued to clamp down on my mind like a vice, suffocating, paralysing.

In that frame of mind I remained for what seemed like hours – hours just lying there, just lying there thinking, thinking thoughts, negative thoughts.

Ever since this morning's incident, negative images had taken possession of me, preying on my mind like a cancer. But now I realized I needed to do something – anything – to rouse myself from this pathetic state; to free myself from the paralysing clutches of doubt, fear, helplessness. I ought to put into practice what I'd learned from the father of positive thinking, Norman Vincent Peale.

"I must think positive . . . I must think positive," I heard myself saying in a determined whisper, the word resounding again and again in my mind.

I searched the reservoir of my mind, the reservoir of hope and optimism that I knew resided deep within me.

"Whatever the mind can conceive and believe, that it can achieve," I whispered slowly, over and over again.

If ever there was a time I needed to believe, that time was now. But no longer was I certain what to believe, or what I believed.

I continued to rake my mind, and I found a good one:

"If ye have faith as a grain of mustard seed, ye shall say unto this mountain, remove hence to yonder place, and it shall remove, and nothing shall be impossible unto you."

I repeated the biblical verse, once, twice, three times. Then I fell silent. I heard the words resonating on their own, echoing through my mind. I considered the verse carefully, word by word, line by line.

"Nothing shall be impossible to you . . . nothing . . ." I felt the words beginning to sink to the depth of my soul.

I believe, I believe.

I closed my eyes. Then opened them. Nothing. Again I closed my eyes. Again I opened them. Nothing. Nothing. Nothing but blackness.

I sucked in a deep shuddering breath.

Relax. Relax. Don't panic.

I felt a horrible tightness gripping my body – my neck, my chest, my arms, my feet. Gripped by such appalling tension, I knew that I stood little chance of releasing my mind from confusion, from distress; little chance of letting the power of belief sink into the deep recesses of my subconscious. I needed to relax, to unwind, to calm the chaotic turbulence of my mind.

I uncoiled myself from the foetal position, sat up in bed and, fumbling in my darkness, reached down, unlaced my shoes, removed them, and tossed them down, unconcerned whether the loud thumps they made on hitting the floor would disturb my landlord.

Then without warning, my head grew suddenly heavy – engulfed in a sickening wave of dizziness. In front of my eyes I saw twinkling stars against a night sky. My head pounded. I needed some Aspirin – maybe four. I had none. Reclining back down, I willed my head to stop spinning.

"I can do all things through Christ who strengthens me," I whispered, grimacing, my thumbs pressing hard against my temples.

It seemed like several heart-wrenching minutes before my darkened world slowed its spinning and came to a reluctant halt.

Breathing a sigh of relief, I gave thanks.

I loosened my collar now, and stretched out upon the little bed. Feet apart, arms at my side, I willed my body, from head to toe, to go limp, to relax.

At that precise moment, from downstairs, I heard the penetrating sound of music and the fast-paced talk of a radio disc-jockey. I recognized the D.J. Tony Blackburn. My favourite. My mind strove to listen.

But immediately I cursed myself for allowing such a distraction to enter my head at a time like this.

I needed to regain focus. I opened my mouth and, tipping back my head, I drew in the deepest breath I could muster. I reeled in my scattered thoughts, mentally shutting out Tony Blackburn and his disc-jockeying.

Then I waggled my feet, vigorously shook my limp arms and rolled my head from side to side. I felt the knotted muscles and ligaments of my neck. I heard the cracks of the bony vertebrae at the base of my skull.

Lying on my back, I raised my right leg, holding it suspended over the bed. Then I brought it back down, directing it to 'let go, let go'.

Moments later, I felt the tension in it easing.

With my left leg, I followed the same routine.

Methodically, I worked my way through the rest of my body: buttocks, thighs, stomach muscles, back, neck, arms, shoulders, jaw, facial muscles. In turn, I tensed each and then relaxed it. I felt the tension oozing from each one, replaced by a warm, calm glow. I sensed my heart rate slowing, my muscles softening. The chaotic panic in my mind had dissolved.

Then I came to my eyes.

I had forgotten my eyes; what was the point in trying to get them to relax?

I can do all things through Christ, who strengthens me, I reminded myself. *I must think positive . . . no negative thoughts.*

With my hands, I covered the sightless pupils, trying to warm them with the heat of my palms. But my palms were cold, chilled. No matter.

"Let go, let go," I murmured.

I continued to feel the tension draining from my body, from my eyes, from my muscles and sinews, and that peaceful warmth growing stronger.

The short, shallow, gasps of breath that had earlier plagued me had now given way to a gentle, free-flowing movement of air into and out of my lungs.

Inhaling deeply, I held my breath, then slowly released it. "Easy, easy, easy," I muttered, enjoying that warm sensation glowing through me.

Now turning my thoughts inward, I pictured my mind as the expansive waters of the Caribbean Sea, the water's wind-swept surface – choppy, turbulent, waves jumping, skipping, crashing into each other. I felt the turbulence within me, my confusion, my despair, my state of total hopelessness, all rushing back. I needed to overcome the turbulent currents.

Whatever the mind can conceive and believe I reminded myself yet again, fearing I was about to lose this battle.

Focusing more precisely now, I directed my brain to relax, relax, relax. Gradually I saw the water's choppy surface settling into stillness. Once again, I felt that blissful serenity sweeping through me. I felt the tension and the turbulence oozing from my mind.

Again I caught my mind entertaining invading thoughts, negative invading thoughts, thoughts that had forced their way in: the dark, frigid, stifling basement room in the Victorian mansion; the corpse on the bed; the McDonald's graveyard shift; my money problems; my head smashing against the door – negative thoughts trying to infiltrate my mind, struggling for readmission. The water's surface once more erupted to turbulence, waves jumping, skipping, crashing. Once more I felt confusion, anguish returning, overwhelming me. I felt my muscles tightening.

The mind can be a secret enemy or a treacherous friend, I had learned. I needed to take control, control of my mind. It was several minutes before I was able to compose myself, regain my equilibrium. Gradually, the waves dissipated to stillness. The negative thoughts struggling to break through, threatening to disrupt my tranquillity, were vanquished. Once again, I felt the stillness, the serenity, as my mind gradually emptied itself of fear, of anxiety, of panic.

Then I began to release my mind, allowing it to drift off freely into the abyss . . .

I was back home, back home in St. Lucia, baretopped, just in blue football shorts, lying on my back, arms outstretched, legs extended – floating, floating aimlessly on the beach, on the giant inflated inner-tube of an old car tire.

I felt my body hovering hazily, aimlessly, in the warm waters of the Malabar beach. I felt the warmth of the sunshine on my skin, tempered by the soothing breeze that rocked the black tube gently from side to side. I heard the mewing of seagulls gliding overhead, the distant faint voices of children playing on the shore, the crrrrrumph! of waves breaking, and their fizzling out into a foaming whiteness that rushed up the sandy shore. I tasted the familiar saltiness of sea water spraying my face. And the scent of suntan lotion from the glistening lobster-red bodies sprawled out along the sand in front of the hotel filled the air.

The inflated rubber tube, like a puffy white cloud in a blue sky, floated aimlessly to and fro on the water's surface, not a care in the world. Free. Totally free.

Smiling gently, quietly, I whispered the words, 'serenity', 'tranquillity', 'peace'. Gradually a state of total peace, of total tranquillity, that now-familiar feeling of weightlessness, overcame me.

The train that passed outside my window felt like a gently rolling breeze. I smiled.

With every fibre of my being, I believed. I believed that whatever the mind can conceive and believe, that it can achieve.

Taking a long, deep breath into my lungs, I brought all my forces together – spiritual, emotional, physical – into one unifying force. I directed the energy towards my eyes, my brain. Feeling in total, absolute control of my mind, my body, my organs, I directed my omnipotent brain – or at least the ten per cent of it that we use – to clear the pathways to my eyes, to release the tension in the muscles, arteries and nerves of my eyes. I instructed my grey matter to take control of my eyes, my retina, my pupils, my arteries.

I felt a warm, tingling sensation slowly seeping through my head, as though my blood vessels were dilating, filling up with the endorphins that my brain was releasing. I sensed coming over me an even more intense inner feeling of warmth, of pleasure, of peace, of joy. I felt the weightlessness of a feather.

With a rush of enthusiasm, I recalled Norman Vincent Peale's words on the power of visualization. *Yes . . . this is what I need to do.*

In my mind I invented all sorts of scenes. Positive scenes; scenes of myself donning a business suit, seated behind a large leather-top mahogany desk in a large carpeted office. I saw myself managing professional staff, leading them, interacting with them. I saw myself out on a field, playing football, cricket, volleyball. I invented pleasant scenes with Susanna and me taking long walks on the beach, holding hands, laughing, chatting.

These scenes were more than fantasy. They were scenes from my future, for I believed Norman Vincent Peale's words: 'Your subconscious mind . . . has a power that turns dreams and aspirations into realities when they are held strong enough. Formulate and stamp indelibly in your mind a mental picture of yourself as succeeding. Hold this picture tenaciously – never permit it to fade. Your mind will seek to deliver'.

These images I'd held for a very long time, but recently they had faded. I brought them back now. They were alive. The images of my future were of a bright and prosperous me. I saw no blindness in my future.

I visualized, and visualized, and visualized. And then slowly – very, very slowly – I felt myself drifting off into a deep, peaceful slumber.

CHAPTER 15

As one rushing train after another rumbled by outside my window, the house rattled around me. The morning rush hour had come early.

I slithered out of bed, took a long hard stretch, roared a trembling yawn, and trudged stiffly across the floor. I reached up and flicked the light switch on, then plodded back groggily towards the bed, thoughts of this morning's classes swirling around in my mind; law and economics today.

If only that law lecturer would . . .

I stopped dead in my tracks, my heart jolting with sudden realization. My body tensed, stiffened. My mind went blank. For a long moment, I just stood there in the middle of the cold room, stunned, perplexed, motionless, flabbergasted, heart pounding.

Yet another train thundered by, its deafening clamour heightening my bewilderment, sharpening the blunt throbbing ache gripping my head.

My mind must surely be playing tricks on me!

I pinched the soft skin on my inside left forearm, but this wasn't one of those dreams or nightmares from which I would suddenly awaken.

Clenching my eyelids shut, I heard not just the words of the prayer rolling off my tongue, but also the pounding of my heart.

I kept my eyes shut, tightly shut, afraid . . . afraid to open them, fearing this was some cruel trick of fate.

Eventually mustering up my courage, I flung my eyelids open and, just as quickly, shut them again. Pulse racing, I continued to plead to the Almighty.

Seconds later, again I jerked my eyes open, and again instantly clamped them shut. My hands shot up to my face, and began rubbing away vigorously at my soft and fleshy prickly eyes.

My heart was beating in my head as I inched my eyes open.

A deep shiver instantly rippled through my body, nearly sending me to my knees for, before me unfolded hazy shapes – vaguely recognisable shapes – blurry outlines – a table, a chair, a bed, a wardrobe, a door . . .

Waves of rapture were running up and down my spine, buffeting my entire body. My eyes were blinking, and blinking, and blinking, again and again; my heart hammered away in my chest.

The faded outlines of the objects began to sharpen, becoming clearer – but only just.

My heart still hammering with fear and hope, gingerly, slowly, I moved about the dim room,

171

touching, feeling, first the bed, then the table, the chair, the door. One by one, I touched the items, fearful that like a mirage they would once more disappear into the dreaded blackness.

But they remained fixed, hard and solid, right there before me. No mirage.

Like a soul condemned to hell but given a last-minute reprieve to heaven, joy exploded in my heart. "Yes! Yes! Yes!" I shouted, punching the air.

"I can see! I can see! Thank you! Thank you Lord God! Thank you!"

My entire being aglow, I crossed myself over and over again, before scurrying across the floor to the blurry table, where I picked up my little orange mirror with its long plastic handle, and surveyed my face.

The image of a battered boxer glared back at me. I held my breath as I stared back at the puffy black eyes, reduced to slits, specks of blood littering their pink surface. The ghastly sight did little to dampen the warm glow of euphoria that consumed me.

"Thank you, Lord Jesus" I breathed, making the sign of the cross once more, feeling the weight of the world lifted off my slender shoulders, feeling joy exploding in my heart.

For a long while, mesmerised, I simply sat there on the edge of the small bed, cold palms resting on my shaking knees, a bright smile dancing merrily upon my face, my chest heaving, ignoring the rush-hour trains roaring past, thinking how wonderful life was. Consumed in this bliss, my mind leaped to St. Lucia – to my sister, to my aunt, to my future wife – knowing that once again I had eyes to see them with. Life was wonderful! I wanted to hug someone – anyone.

I couldn't thank God enough, for today I had seen His amazing grace.

I hadn't forgotten Norman Vincent Peale. I thanked him, too. For a fleeting instant, though, it dimly occurred to me that perhaps positive thinking might have been merely a placebo, that positive thinking or not I would still have regained my eyesight. No matter. That's the power of belief. The power of faith, the evidence of things unseen. And to me, that was the bottom line of all bottom lines.

Later that morning, still blissfully aglow, but plagued with creeping anxiety, and with eyes swollen, black and bloodshot, I strode into the GP's office off Lewisham Way, expecting some answers, some reassurances. All I got was a blood-pressure reading, and a referral to an optician.

Two bus rides – and countless fleeting, awkward stares from passengers – later, I strode into the small reception area on the ground floor of a three-storey nondescript Harley Street building. The obese, bespectacled auburn-haired young woman behind the reception desk casually glanced up at me from her magazine. Instantly I saw the alarm go off in her eyes.

After I'd explained my problem to her, with a

sympathetic look she promised to do all in her power to ensure the doctor attended to me today. She strode off into a back room, and several anxious minutes later returned to her desk, a slight smile pulling at the corners of her mouth. Though she hadn't given me the verdict, I felt cautiously optimistic and sent her a smile, which she returned demurely before shifting her gaze back to the magazine on the desk before her.

When, moments later, a short, balding, white-coated, Indian man with a stethoscope around his neck, stepped through his office door to greet me, I could have sworn that the sight of me put a pause into his step. His dark, rotund face instantly lost all its animation as his eyes studied my face. His forehead began to wrinkle into a worry frown.

He introduced himself as Dr. Basu, and ushered me into a small, sterile room, motioning me to the long, black articulated chair in the middle of the room.

I found intimidating anything that brought to mind my three-month stint at Victoria Hospital in St. Lucia, not least doctors' consulting rooms. This was no exception. It didn't help when the optician, that worry-frown still creasing his forehead, switched off the wall lights, and peered into my bloodshot eyes using a sharp, piercing light that almost regenerated my blindness.

Biting my lip, I felt the warmth of the man's tobacco-breath on my face, his trembling thumb and index finger stabilising my tilted head as he continued to peer into my eyes in studied silence, seemingly doing more damage than good.

"You taking any prescription medicines?" he asked, in a thick accent I couldn't trace.

"No," I muttered, willing him to turn off the piercing white light.

His tobacco-scented hand tilted my head farther backwards. "Look to your left, please."

He fiddled with a dial on his equipment. It made a clicking sound like an alarm clock being wound up. "Got high blood pressure?"

"Don't think so."

"Mmm," he breathed. "Right, please. How about diabetes? Look up!"

"No . . . don't know . . . umm . . . my grandmother died of diabetes."

He stood back, and much to my eyes' relief, switched off the light. After flicking the wall lights back on, he took a seat in the swivel chair across from me, next to a metal-top desk.

He stared me straight in the eye, frowning in concern. "Have you been under severe stress lately?"

I responded after a moment's hesitation, "Yes . . . life has been a bit stressful . . . a bit."

The optician then listened intently as I recounted, as instructed, the series of events leading to my temporary loss of sight. As I trailed off, he reached into his desk draw, extracted a Velcro armband and proceeded to take my blood pressure; my second such reading today.

"So what caused this, Doc?"

He set the Velcro sleeve down on the desk. "It could have been any number of things."

I studied his dark face for any hints of concern, hoping the creases on his forehead were permanent frown lines.

"It is possible that you may have suffered a blockage of blood flow to your eyes."

I frowned: "A blockage?"

"Yes. There are two arteries, one on each side of the neck, which are connected to even smaller arteries that deliver blood from the heart to the eyes and brain. Debris from deposits on the walls of the arteries could break off and travel through these smaller branches to the eyes, and this could block the blood flow within those smaller vessels."

In his strange accent, steady and calm, the doctor explained further, drawing on a piece of paper to illustrate.

I listened intently, trying to make sense of the pencil-sketch.

"The arteries of the eyes can also be affected by increased pressure in the brain, which in turn increases pressure on the optic nerve. Migraine headaches can also be a culprit; this can cause spasms and narrowing in the arteries of the eye."

He paused, frowning that frown, staring me straight in the eye. "Do you suffer from migraines?"

"No . . . never," I said, hoping that my chronic sinus headaches weren't migraines.

"Anyway," he continued, "the blow to your head may have somehow caused a blockage, preventing the blood from flowing to your eyes."

He paused a moment, then said, "The most common symptom of restricted blood-flow to the eyes is sudden blindness. But this usually goes away quickly. In fact it is usually in one eye only and lasts from seconds to minutes."

He shook his head slowly, fixing his eyes firmly on me, a look of apprehension crossing his face. "Yours was a rare occurrence, because not only did it affect both eyes, but also because it lasted for more than twenty-four hours."

"Why do you think, Doc?"

He sighed. "Again, I can only speculate on that. The trauma of the blow to your head could have put additional pressure on the arteries, which were probably already weakened by your stressful lifestyle. There might have been a temporary blockage, and the resulting pressure may have ruptured the arteries, causing blood to leak into your eyes."

He pointed to my eye. "This would explain the blood deposits in and around your eyes. The black eye is actually caused by dead blood seeping into the tissues around your eye – nothing to worry about; it should clear up in a matter of days."

I sighed, sitting back, feeling a great deal lighter. "Okay."

"I have only seen a case like yours twice in my ten-year career," the optician continued, "and one of the patients, who sustained a severe blow to his head in a motor vehicle accident, remains blind to this very day."

My heart skipped a beat.

"I think you should consider yourself a very, very lucky young man," said the doctor, pronouncing his 'V' as 'W'.

He prescribed some eye-drops, and suggested lots of rest, a diet rich in Vitamin A, and a follow-up visit with him.

He ushered me out through to the small reception area, asking the kindly young lady behind the desk to pencil me in for next week. I thanked her for her help, and strode out through the glass door, into the cold, to await bus Number Thirty-six.

Over the next three days, I remained mainly indoors, feasting on a diet of scrambled eggs, toast, and carrot juice. Though the dizziness had subsided and the prickly sensation in my eyes had all but ebbed away, bright lights still hurt my eyes.

As my black and bloodshot eyes cleared up, the swelling flattened, and my vision returned to normal, against my better judgement I decided against keeping my date with Dr. Basu.

A day or two later, lying on my bed with my hands linked firmly behind my neck, I stumbled upon what I considered the answers to the multitude of questions swirling around in my head. Keen on capturing this fleeting moment of enlightenment, I quickly reached across to my side table, picked up my pen, and the little black book into which I habitually scrawled my thoughts.

My pen scribbled away:

*This experience was a signal – an act of divine
intervention. I was on the wrong track and needed
to be brought back on course. Staying on this path
would have led to disaster. Thank God, I have been
warned – I now need to change course.*

As my blue PaperMate pen sped furiously
across the paper, I was reminded of my two
common entrance exam failures that had paved
the way for my entry into the SDA Academy.
These, too, my mind concluded, were acts of divine
intervention.

The Creator had a plan for me, I told myself. In
time, I'd see the results.

I set my pen resolutely on the paper; it began to
scratch away furiously:

*Going to college was a mistake. I do not need to
go to college to become a qualified accountant. I do
not need to be tutored – I will teach myself
accounting. I will quit college.*

*Here I am, in the City of London, the financial
centre of the world; I need to be out there, gaining
invaluable experience. An accountancy qualification means little without solid practical experience.
I need to prepare for that job back home.*

Atop a fresh page, I wrote the word: RESOLU-
TIONS, underlined it twice and, beneath it, scribbled the following:

> *Quit college*
> *Quit McDonald's*
> *Get a job in the City*
> *Study like crazy in the evenings / weekends*
> *Take exams – no tutoring*

Then I stopped, and thought long and hard about what I'd just written. I'd set myself a real challenge . . . I'd be competing against full-time students. The pass rate for accountancy exams, I recalled, was around thirty per cent . . . seven out of ten students were destined to fail at each sitting. Studying on my own would be akin to pushing a huge boulder single-handed up a slippery hill while those in full-time study whizzed by in their heavy-traction vehicles.

But with every fibre of my being, I felt empowered – believing I could do anything I put my mind to . . . anything my mind can conceive, that it can achieve.

My slender blue PaperMate continued to glide along:

- *Gaining experience and passing exams are equally important tasks.*
- *I will find time for rest and relaxation – time for a social life. Pursuing a qualification should not mean that life is on hold; it is part of life's experience, and I should savour the taste of this opportunity.*
- *Regular visits to Hyde Park Corner.*
- *Practise positive thinking and visualization.*

I set the pen down on the table, rose to my feet, took a long hard stretch, and began to pace about the room, feeling a deep frown of concentration creasing my forehead.

With deep resolve in my voice, aloud I said, "It's time for me to take my rightful place in the world . . . time for me to fulfil my destiny."

CHAPTER 16

Briefcase firmly in hand, I strutted down Farringdon Road, feeling every bit on top of my game. The crisp spring air surrounded me, sharpening my focus for the challenge ahead.

Along the pavement teeming with people darting about in every direction, ultra-modern, glass-fronted buildings rose up like great plinths of glass and steel, shimmering in the morning sunshine. Glistening black London cabs pulled up alongside the curb, releasing besuited occupants who paid no heed to the young men in jeans and tee-shirts standing on the pavements, proffering copies of *Time Out* magazine. On street corners, casually clad men and women stood in small wooden kiosks festooned with colourful magazines, postcards, newspapers, and confectionery. Not unlike auctioneers, these vendors cried out in rapid-fire cockney, waving newspapers. Every now and then a passer-by would stop briefly, throw some loose change into plastic pots set on a news-stand counter, and pick up a paper or two. The pink broadsheet paper, which I recognised as the *Financial Times*, seemed a favourite.

All around me, men and women with blank expressions, professionally attired in dark suits and sporting leather briefcases, powered their way through the hustle and bustle, as though running late for some crucial appointment.

Unsmiling, I admired my image in a *United Colours of Benetton* shop window as I swaggered by, noting that my Afro added an inch or two to my slender, six-foot frame. I had traded my McDonald's uniform for a navy blue single-breasted jacket over a light blue shirt and dark blue cotton tie. All three items had cost me just over twenty pounds at *Mr Byrite*. It could easily have been a more expensive shopping spree had I not resurrected an old pair of work trousers, saving myself twenty pounds. I hadn't been terribly bothered that my trousers were a shade or two lighter than my knee-length jacket. Now, feeling the chilled breeze penetrating the flimsy material, assaulting my ankles, above which my trousers fell, I questioned the wisdom of not getting a new pair.

Despite the bright sunshine, the air felt chilly. At the last minute, feeling that it did little to bolster my image, I'd decided to leave my winter jacket hanging in the wardrobe. I'd taken adequate precautions, however, against the cold. Under my shirt, I'd insulated my body with two thermal tee-shirts over a thick cotton vest. I looked a little stuffed, but I had no qualms about that; I could do with a few extra pounds on my bones.

As I strutted along, I caught another glimpse of myself, this time in the glass façade of an Italian restaurant. Slowing a little, I straightened my tie, squared my shoulders, and tightened the grip on my first-ever briefcase. It mattered little that it had a shiny plastic covering, and had set me back a mere ten pounds at W H Smith. Neither did it matter that it contained only a PaperMate ballpoint pen, a Casio scientific calculator, and a free copy of *Time Out*. All that really mattered to me was that I was on my way . . . on my way to the Big Time.

I felt a deep sense of satisfaction with life, and couldn't keep a slight smile off my face as I strutted along, for I was on my way to join the élite. I vowed that as soon as the money started pouring in, I'd buy one of those professional-looking suits, and perhaps a new briefcase, a leather one. And, of course, I needed to touch up my hair a little – jerry curls or something.

As I rounded the corner from Holborn Tube station into Southampton Row, the crowds thickened and the pace quickened. Taking deep breaths into my lungs and exhaling slowly, I tried to calm my now simmering nerves. The challenge I was heading towards would be my first big test. There was no room for failure.

Reed Accountancy – the recruitment agency providing accounting staff to companies across the UK – were suitably impressed with my CV. A stint, however brief, at one of the world's top accountancy firms, seemed an invaluable asset in London. Coopers & Lybrand was closer to the top than most, and it seemed to matter little that my fifteen months' experience was restricted to a tiny Caribbean island. My previous part-time bookkeeping job in Catford – a few minutes up the road from my Lewisham bedsit – carried very little weight; my auditing experience was what had done the trick.

Although I was initially concerned about work-permit requirements, once I had stated that my mother and father were both British citizens, the topic never arose. With my experience and the marketability it offered, I opted for temporary accounting assignments which afforded me the flexibility to prepare, at my own pace, for the gruelling twice-yearly exams.

Nancy, an attractive, petite brunette in her early thirties, had been assigned as my personal agent. She all but guaranteed me continuous, challenging assignments with prestigious City clients – assignments promising invaluable accounting experience that should prepare me for that leading financial role that I knew, in my heart of hearts, awaited me back home.

Now, standing before the impressive granite-façade multi-storey building, I felt a nervous smile twitching my lips. I adjusted my tie, took in a deep, invigorating breath, and strode towards the entranceway.

The automatic revolving doors hissed open,

revealing a foyer, the grandeur of which I had never before seen the like. As I entered, glancing to my left, I saw an exquisite seating area with blue upholstered chairs arranged around a marble-top coffee table with an assortment of newspapers. Thriving potted plants stood in every corner, their distinctive waxy leaves glistening in the bright fluorescent lighting.

I strode across the floor, shooting a glance to my left at the heavy-set, middle-aged man seated in the waiting area. A copy of the *Financial Times* held up before his eyes, he flicked a glance at his watch, frowned, looked up at the wall clock, frowned again, and returned his gaze to the pink broadsheet newspaper. The man exuded power. I promised myself to get one of those double-breasted suits as soon as I was able to, but one without those pin stripes. Someone recently remarked to me that pin-stripe suits presented a gangster image – a far cry from the look I intended to portray.

My eyes flicked glances at the men and women bustling past, making their way through one set of automatic double doors towards another on the far side of the reception hall.

I checked the wall clock. Nine fifteen. Right on time.

Almost feeling myself ascending to a higher station in life, I squared my shoulders and strode briskly to the angular granite reception counter, and to the fine-looking blonde in a charcoal-grey business suit who sat behind the counter.

"Good morning; I am Rudy from Reed Accountancy. I'm here to see Mr Henry," I said, much as I had rehearsed time and again in front of my mirror. Staring into the pale blue eyes, my smile tried to exude confidence.

The young lady ran her eyes over my jacket, and in a distinctly refined London accent, said, "Okay, sir, he will be right with you . . . please take a seat."

She checked a little black book on the counter in front of her, picked up the telephone, and announced my arrival to someone.

Long minutes ticked by.

I was pondering whether blondes really do have more fun, when a gentleman in a well-cut ash-grey suit, appeared before me.

For what seemed a long moment, through thick glasses his hazel eyes studied me appraisingly.

"Rudy?" he said finally, offering his hand.

"Yes . . . Mr Henry?" I flashed a smile as I rose to greet the accountant seemingly in his late thirties, of average height, with round shoulders, and hair the colour of sand.

During our quick but firm handshake, I found myself hoping he would have no difficulty understanding my Caribbean accent, an accent I'd tried to neutralize through hours of practice, listening to British politicians and BBC reporters. I was sick and tired of being asked to repeat myself; in a professional environment I couldn't allow such impediments to hamper my development.

"Please follow me," he said, in a clipped voice.

He turned on his heel, and strode back briskly through the large glass door which slid open as we approached and hissed shut behind us. I followed my host along a brightly lit corridor, past several large rooms with vacant desks. On the magnolia walls along the hallway were faded newspaper clippings encased in glass frames, presumably depicting the company's history and achievements.

Pulling open the fire door at the end of the corridor, the man, who hadn't uttered a word since our meeting in the reception area, stepped back to allow me into a medium-sized, carpeted office. Then he motioned me to a seat at a beige metal desk.

Poker-faced, Mr. Henry pulled up a chair, sat next to me, and in a piping voice, complained about the backlog of invoices that had built up since the accounts payable clerk had succumbed to the flu over two weeks previously. Suppliers were being paid late or not at all. This lapse had put the company into a bad light, sending the wrong signals to the market; the directors were embarrassed.

I studied his face as he spoke. He seemed troubled, burdened, like one whose job hung in the balance. I understood. I empathized. I wanted desperately to help him out of this jam.

But then I saw it. The ghastly contraption that stood on the side desk next to the accountant, and which shot a bolt of fear right through me. My confidence vanished as suddenly as a light bulb switched off.

Shivers of apprehension were dancing down my

spine, a silent onrush of panic began to grip me. I could feel the palms of my hands sweating.

Only once before had I laid eyes on such a machine. Thankfully, back then we had both maintained a respectable distance from each other. I stayed my ground in the general office getting on with my work; the grisly machine had remained under plastic covering, locked away in the small boardroom at Coopers & Lybrand. I liked it that way.

Then I heard the clipped voice say, "I need you to input the invoices into the Bought Ledger."

My heart skipped a beat, and I felt a horrible plummeting in my stomach, as if plunging down a deep dark hole. For what seemed a long bewildering moment, my brain stalled: I struggled to remember my name, and why I was sitting before this white man with troubled eyes and thinning sandy hair.

"Input?" I said, after a long moment, sweat dampening my body, a feeling of trepidation rising like bile in my throat.

Gazing at me over thick glasses, my client gestured to the machine on the desk. "Yes . . . on the computer."

I concentrated all my will on trying to subdue the pounding of my heart.

"On the . . . the . . . com . . . com . . . puter?" I heard myself whimper.

Mr Henry studied me with tired, heavy-lidded, speculative grey eyes: "Yes."

After a moment's hesitation during which I fought down the urge to grab my briefcase from under the desk and dash out the room, in a faltering tone I said, "I'm sorry Mr Henry, but I . . . I have never . . . um . . . never actually . . . um . . . used one of those . . . um . . . those things before. Never."

Feeling my world falling apart, I wished desperately that I was back at my little table in my chilly room, my eyes glued to my accounting texts under the bright desk lamp.

The accountant squinted at me as though he'd just discovered I could neither read nor write. "It's very easy, I can assure you."

"I'm sure I . . . I . . . can do it better . . . manually," I offered, dragging my voice through the strangling mortification in my chest.

He shook his head dismissively, rose from his seat, and set a pale, bony hand atop the blinking, monochrome monitor.

"Our accounting system is now fully computerised," he said. "For a while we did run a parallel manual system, but I'm afraid we have now gone live."

Tapping the machine, he continued. "We have invested significant sums in this state-of–the-art computer, one of the most powerful in the world. It is an IBM 5150 microcomputer, with 16KB RAM and 64KB ROM with a MS-DOS operating system."

He had lost me. The man was speaking a foreign language.

"I really don't know how . . . how to use it," I

said in a weak apologetic voice, feeling my face growing hotter and hotter as my gaze swept over the horrible contraption . . . that . . . that thing . . . the computer.

A bead of sweat formed just below my hairline. I quickly wiped it away with the back of my hand, wishing for an earthquake or something . . . anything to get me out of there.

A look of annoyance came over the accountant's face. "Let me show you."

I sat awkwardly before the computer, listening to the accountant, who was leaning over me, tapping the keyboard, explaining the input process: the input fields, the date, the invoice number, the batch number, the supplier code, the VAT code, the value, the return key, the save function.

I listened, hardly hearing, hardly seeing, distracted by torrential thoughts of failure swirling around in my mind.

When Mr Henry disappeared into the adjoining office, leaving a mountain of invoices in the wire in-tray on the desk before me, not for the first time, I wondered what mess I'd got myself into. I felt dumb, lost, not unlike a Neanderthal who had suddenly found himself at the controls of a space ship.

For a long while, I just sat there, at the desk, in front of the computer, listlessly staring at the flickering monochrome screen, feeling panic rising from the pit of my stomach. In the cool room, I felt my body dampened with sweat. I didn't need a mirror to know my face had gone bright red.

With bated breath, I reached out a quivering index finger and pressed a key with an imprint of an upturned arrow. In horror, I watched as the screen started to move up and up and up, right there before my eyes. I pressed another, but that only made things worse, for the screen then began to move sideways; a third key, and I heard a sharp beep.

"Oh, my god . . . I've destroyed the damn thing," I muttered, casting a swift glance over my shoulder to make sure that no one had witnessed my act of vandalism.

My heart pounding hard and fast under my ribs, the back of my hand tried, but couldn't keep up with, the sweat beading my forehead.

In my mind I screamed *Help!*

Up until now, with my scientific calculator and adding machine, I'd been certain I could survive the vagaries of my chosen profession. In accountancy magazines, I had read, more than once, that the computer was the future of accounting. Some pundits even suggested that accountants were destined for the scrap-heap, soon to be rendered obsolete by the emerging technology. A little voice in the back of my head had consistently whispered to me that some day, I would come face to face with the mortal enemy.

But why now? I heard myself thinking. *Why now? Why couldn't the man have given me some manual bank reconciliations to do?*

Five devastating minutes later, I was back on Southampton Row, sullen, trudging on shaky legs towards Holborn tube station, eyeing the pavement, willing it to open up and swallow me.

But it was self-consciousness that consumed me. My Afro; my cheap, ill-fitting jacket; my off-colour, ankle-length trousers; my plastic briefcase . . . everything . . . everything – including my silly swagger – made me feel out of place, conspicuous, a mango placed on a pile of apples.

Three minutes earlier, Nancy, my agent, had called, sounding sympathetic but disappointed . . . disappointed in me. Mr Henry had phoned her, seething with rage. He demanded that I be immediately replaced. I wasn't suited for the job . . .

I had failed . . . miserably.

CHAPTER 17

"Snakes and ladders," I kept thinking, as the crowded train boisterously rattled its way through the subterranean tunnels, oblivious to the hustle and bustle in the streets of London, up above.

"This is what life is . . . a game of snakes and ladders," I mused. "One moment you're full of hope . . . climbing a sturdy ladder . . . the next moment, fickle fate gives you a shove, sending you sliding down the slithery snake of despair."

I eyed the worn, slatted wooden floor, reverberating from the sheer velocity of the train. I felt a dismal failure.

Perhaps I'd bitten off more than I could chew. Perhaps I should have listened to the wiser, older West Indian; upon hearing of my ambitious plans for the City, my landlord had peered at me with undisguised scepticism, if not annoyance.

My mind replayed our conversation.

"How could you, a little country boy from the Caribbean, hope to come to this white man's country and get a proper job, with so many British people out of work? You know how long it take me to get to where I am today? I'm a technician at British Petroleum, you know."

I had maintained a respectable silence in the presence of the older man, who continued, his voice uncharacteristically raised.

"Young man, it took me almost thirty years!" He exclaimed. "Thirty years!"

He glared at me as if trying to read my reaction, then added, "Man, you must be crazy, expecting to come here and make it in just a few months!"

At that point, I'd realised my mistake in revealing my plans; I'd just needed someone to talk to.

In a sharp Barbadian accent, the heavyset, middle-aged, dark-skinned man continued his rant. "Rudy, my advice to you is to stop dreaming. Stay in college, get your qualification, and then go back home . . . where you belong."

It was my turn to look incredulous.

"This is a white man's country . . . we cannot behave like one of them . . . we must know our place." His tone was clipped, final.

I'd dismissed my landlord's misgivings, vowing to prove him wrong. I'd also vowed never again to reveal or to discuss my ambitions, particularly with those who didn't share my values, my aspirations. But now, it seemed the wiser, older man was, after all . . . right.

*   *   *

The ride back home seemed interminable. Negative thoughts assailed me, hovering around in my mind, like ghosts.

It was my first big chance. I had blown it. Was it back to the dreaded graveyard shift at McDonald's? Would I ever rebound from this? Had I failed my agent, Reed Accountancy? Had they lost faith in me?

Slouched in the cushioned seat in a middle carriage of the noisy, crammed, underground train, I stared into oblivion, ignoring the slurping sounds coming from the young couple embraced in a passionate kiss next to me.

I felt neither powerful nor positive. No point digging into my briefcase for my well-thumbed copy of *The Power of Positive Thinking*. I hadn't planned on any motivational reading today. My briefcase still had in it only a calculator, a pen, and *Time Out*.

The train screeched to a halt at Chancery Lane. Passengers rose to disembark. My eyes left the floor and caught a glimpse of the kissing, slurping couple who'd sat next to me as they rose to get off the train. The young man, with short, spiky jet-black hair, and a neatly trimmed, conjoined beard and moustache, wore a red Arsenal tee-shirt – number eleven. His partner, clasping his hand, was slim . . . very slim . . . slim and narrow . . . from the back.

What I then saw stunned me.

I sat, my mouth agape.

The young man's partner also wore a similarly styled moustache and beard. For the past few minutes, I had been seating next to . . . next to two men . . . two men making out.

Although gay sex had been made legal between consenting adults in England, such a public demonstration took me completely off-guard. I couldn't quell the wave of nausea welling up in my stomach. I needed some Andrew's or Eno's, but I had none. I tried to think pleasant, off-setting thoughts. I could find none.

Several unsettling minutes elapsed before I was able to compose myself.

Up until now, my biggest defeat had been twice failing my common entrance exams. That was light years ago; it had floored me, but I had rebounded.

To deal with this new crisis, I needed my Emergency Kit.

Though considering myself an incurable optimist, I wasn't fooled into thinking that along the path to success, failure wouldn't periodically rear its ugly head. Despite *Positive Thinking*, I had always known full well that I would need to fortify myself further to handle the ravages that might, from time to time, threaten to throw me off course, veering me onto the road to ruin. No stranger to failure, I knew I needed to prepare, to build within me, the internal fortitude to cope with those potential disasters, even when none was visible on the horizon.

In my motivational readings, I hadn't shied away from learning to manage failure. I had learned that in winning the war several battles may have to be fought, some of which may be lost. That it is during the times of peace that armies are strengthened in preparation for war. That one who does not prepare for hurricanes when none threatens is lacking in wisdom and foresight. Failure and disaster may be delayed, even over long periods, but sometimes they may be inevitable . . . sometimes even necessary.

Those thoughts were strengthened after my recent bout of temporary blindness. It had struck me that I needed to do much more to fortify myself.

To that end I had set out to prepare myself, to buttress myself inwardly, in spirit and in mind, so that when bouts of failure came a-calling, I would have in reserve the necessary internal fortitude to respond appropriately.

And so, I'd set out to build my emergency kit. I had spent countless hours at the Lewisham Central Library, studying the lives and achievements of great men: men who had experienced failure and difficulties along their path to success; men who had risen above their failure and difficulties; men from whom I could learn a thing or two about life.

The train screeched into Bank station. A disembodied male voice repeatedly cautioned passengers to 'mind the gap'. As the doors hissed shut and the train pulled away from the platform, my upbringing told me it would be right to offer my seat to the heavily pregnant lady who stood near my seat in the crowded train, clinging to an overhead chrome pendant, for support. Her abdomen protruded way beyond her unbuttoned overcoat, her face tired and depressed.

As the woman, seemingly in her early thirties, staggered with the train's movement, I felt discomfited, tormented by my lack of gallantry. I hoisted myself up and offered my seat.

She fixed her hazel eyes sternly upon me. Then within earshot of surrounding passengers, she said, "You're rather chauvinistic aren't you? I'm sure you only offered me your seat because I'm a woman."

I blinked, staring at her in stunned amazement.

"No," I replied after a moment's hesitation, speaking with equal vigour, and maintaining a straight face. "I would also have offered it to a pregnant man."

The woman's pale face went bright red. She made no attempt to reply.

I sat back down, hearing indistinguishable sounds of humour rising around me, muffled giggles, choked-back laughter, clearing of throats.

Back home now, in the relative sanctuary of my bed-sit, I heaved a sigh of relief that my landlord wasn't at home to witness my dishonourable return. He would have sniggered at the sight of me, still fresh from the Caribbean, with an untamed Afro, sporting my ill-fitting suit, cheap shiny-brown plastic briefcase in hand.

Taking a deep breath and letting it out slowly, I reached across the table, picking up the bright orange lever arch file with a sticky label bearing the crudely-lettered words: EMERGENCY KIT.

Elbows digging into the table, fists buried in my cheeks, in pensive silence I read the contents of the first insert – an inspirational poem by an unknown author:

When things go wrong, as they sometimes will,
When the road you're trudging seems all uphill
When the funds are low and the debts are high
And you want to smile, but you have to sigh.

When care is pressing you down a bit
Rest if you must, but don't you quit
Life is queer with its twists and turns,
As every one of us sometimes learns,
And many a failure turns about
When he might have won had he stuck it out
Don't give up, though the pace seems slow
You may succeed with another blow!

Success is failure turned inside out –
The silver tint of the clouds of doubt,
And you can never tell how close you are,
It may be near when it seems so far.

So stick to the fight when you're hardest hit –
It's when things seem worse that you must not quit.

Again and again I read through it, the verses flowing from my lips like a song.

"I need to stick to the fight," I whispered, allowing the words to resonate of their own accord. I barely paid any heed to the roaring train passing outside my window.

Flipping to the next page, I read the words of Booker T. Washington, an ex-slave in plantation America, who had achieved a great deal of success.

Success is to be measured not so much by the position that one has reached in life, as by the obstacles which he has overcome while trying to succeed.

Having read through the paragraph a third time, I paused, closing my eyes, allowing the words to resound in my head. I felt creeping redemption.

Overleaf, my eyes scanned the inspiring words of Thomas Carlyle, the British historian and essayist from Victorian times:

Obstacles in the pathway of the weak become stepping stones in the pathway of the strong.

Another train thundered by. I hardly blinked.

An old Russian proverb came to mind: 'a hammer shatters glass, but forges steel'. I needed to become steel.

As I turned to my favourite section of the kit, I felt growing confidence, a smile broadening. I delighted in reading biographies of the great.

Thomas Edison, one of the greatest inventors of all time, held over one thousand patents. His most widely acclaimed device, the incandescent light bulb, was an invention he perfected because of his sheer tenacity and determination to make it work. Edison experienced more than one thousand failures in developing a filament for the bulb. He tested more than sixteen hundred different materials and then six thousand types of fibre, before discovering that a cotton thread coated with carbon would work, and so would bamboo. It then took another ten years of failure to develop the storage battery, with more than ten thousand unsuccessful experiments. But in the end, the great man triumphed.

Increasingly elated, feeling adrenalin coursing through my veins, next I read about the founder of FedEx – Fred Smith.

Before succeeding in building his package-delivery empire, Smith had been plagued with a host of failures and catastrophes. His family had accused him of frittering away the family fortune, and then disowned him. For the first three years of operation, Smith's company had made huge losses and seemed always on the verge of bankruptcy. On one occasion, the hard-pressed businessman had had to fall back on his gambling proceeds to meet his payroll costs. To make matters worse, Smith became the subject of an FBI investigation, faced many lawsuits, and a bitter divorce. Losing his job as CEO of his own company was a bitter blow. He refused to give up, however, struggling on and on, eventually making FedEx one of the world's most successful companies.

Reading those words I felt a rebirth, a new beginning. Suddenly I felt less devastated about failing my first temporary accounting assignment. Failure was an indispensable part of life, I reassured myself. I was steel, not glass. *This experience has forged me – it hasn't broken me.*

But I needed to eliminate the gaps in my skills set.

As I sat at my little desk, deep in thought, chewing my lips, not for the first time I found myself believing that somehow, someway, I was divinely guided. The Lord above was telling me something . . . that it was time to neutralize my enemy, that ghastly contraption called the computer. No longer would it intimidate me. I would conquer it. I would defeat that mocking, winking cursor, and, as in war, the defeated enemy would be put to my service, for life, as an indispensable tool of trade.

Chin up, with a determined stride, I sallied forth once more into the world of business. This time my footsteps led to Lewisham Central Library, and to the technology shelves labelled C.

I was determined to rise up, like the phoenix, from the ashes.

CHAPTER 18

"Margaret Thatcher's a bloody whore!" the short-legged, large-bellied man bellowed, his voice simmering with rage.

Perched on his wooden crate, ranting at a crowd of about fifty disparate souls ranged loosely before him, the man had a throaty cockney accent that was barely decipherable. His pale, rotund face, highlighted by the livid crimson of his cheeks, glistened with sweat, and from time to time, with an irritation I found amusing, his short, fat fingers slapped off his sticky face stray strands of his long, bleached-blond hair, mostly pulled back in a messy pony-tail.

The recent British and American bombing raids over Libya hadn't gone down well in the UK. The speaker was incensed. The Prime Minister's unholy alliance with President Bush was nothing short of an abomination, according to this belligerent middle-aged man who, only minutes before, had been merely another squabbling member of the rowdy crowd.

Amid the throng, I looked on in stunned amazement as the protestor continued on his rampage, accentuated by wild swinging gestures and spontaneous expletives, the seat of his ill-fitting, faded blue jeans sagging low, his drenched white tee-shirt stretched tightly across his belly above his protruding navel, revealing a bulbous expanse of soggy white flesh.

My amazement lay in the fact that this commotion was happening less than a mile from Parliament, and from No. 10 Downing Street, the official residence of the British Prime Minister. From his makeshift stage, the pony-tailed man hurled obscene insults at the 'Iron Lady', knowing full well that his right to speak his mind – especially on this small piece of historical real estate – was virtually guaranteed.

Averting my eyes from the belligerent, self-proclaimed anarchist, I squinted out at the lush, expansive landscape behind him. Hyde Park, a mile and a half long, half a mile wide, boasted three hundred and forty acres of woods, grasslands, lake and gardens, all smack in the centre of London.

But it was this north-eastern portion of Hyde Park that most fascinated me. Hyde Park Corner, or Speakers' Corner as it is widely known, was established as a place for free speech by an Act of Parliament in 1872. Every Sunday since then, people from all walks of life – from crackpots to misunderstood geniuses – have turned up there unannounced to give the wandering crowds a glimpse of their mind. It was with no little amazement that I learned that the likes of Lenin, Karl Marx, George Orwell and Marcus Garvey had graced the makeshift stages of this bastion of free speech.

My eyes surveyed my immediate surroundings. All over, speakers elevated on makeshift platforms of soap boxes, crates, step ladders and the like could be seen and heard striving to engage the fickle, footloose spectators, with everything from calls to revolution to warnings of personal damnation.

Today was just another typical spring Sunday for me. Up at five, hit the books till two, short break for lunch. An afternoon at Hyde Park Corner was my way of relaxing, my way of recharging my batteries, my way of preparing for the challenges of the week ahead. A little laughter and some thought-provoking insights seldom failed to get me off to a good start. And for what lay ahead this coming week, I desperately needed a good start.

As the sun vanished behind a heap of cloud, turning the spring day dull, my eyes travelled back to the animated man, now calling for the assassination of 'Thatcher' and 'Bush'.

I noted none of the usual hecklers engaged in the usual battle of wit and will, trying to intimidate and disrupt the speaker. Quite unusual, I thought, for heckling was an established and accepted tradition at Speakers' Corner. Had Prime Minister Thatcher got it right?

A cool breeze hissed by, rustling the collar of my thick jacket. It felt comforting, to be outdoors once more. Inhaling deeply, I felt the mint coolness rushing through my nostrils, down inside my lungs, invigorating.

Having had a bellyful of Thatcher- and Bush-bashing, it was time for me to seek out new amusements. Hands tucked firmly in my trouser pockets, I strolled casually along, weaving my way through scatterings of tourists and other onlookers. All over the park, spring flowers had burst into bloom, filling my eyes and nose with their rainbow colours and delicious scents.

The bespectacled, grey-haired, matronly woman in a long white dress, who stood, without an audience, banging a tambourine and screaming 'Rock of Ages', didn't tickle me the least bit. I moved on, pleased that the sun had broken through the clouds again, the light spilling over the entire park. As I often did, I marvelled that the London sunshine always seemed devoid of heat . . . in springtime, at least.

Moments later I stood on the fringes of a small gathering, gazing upon the antics of a short, obese, grey-haired woman dressed as a nun, perched on a plastic bench, yelling at her thoroughly amused audience massed before her.

"God will get you . . . you sick, sinful, bastards!" she chided, in a gushing falsetto voice.

Laughter swept the mass.

I watched, amused, as more and more 'sinful bastards' congregated. After fifteen hilarious minutes or so, the crowd had swelled to about fifty.

Barely stifling my laughter, shoulders heaving up and down, I gazed on, amazed, as those seemingly masochistic bystanders took turns confessing their sins in return for the dubious pleasure of receiving a spontaneous rebuke.

"Holy Mother . . . last night I slept with my ninety-year-old blind grandmother," a pleading male Irish voice confessed.

"Prepare!" the obese lady snapped, her voice rolling out like a muted clap of thunder, ". . . to be shafted . . . in your anus . . . by Satan . . . in hell!"

Fits of laughter rippled through the expectant crowd. And twenty minutes of hysteria had passed before my eyes wandered to a small throng congregated under an unlit lamp post in the relatively stark sunshine. Most of the women wore black and had even their faces covered. The men wore long white robes, and some wore colourful hats that looked like small upside-down flower pots. I assumed these people were Muslims.

I moved in closer. The central figure, straddled on a stack of crates, a red bandana wrapped tightly around his sweat-dampened forehead, his face red with fury, was raging militantly in some strange language. Though I couldn't understand his words, I did understand the hatred in his fierce dark eyes, directed at a middle-aged white man who stood six or so yards away, a travel bag flung over his shoulders. Sensing the crowd's hostility, the white man drifted away.

Imaging that I was next in line for a dose of the militant's venom, I followed suit.

When I got to within earshot of the impeccably-dressed middle-aged man shouting at an impressive crowd under the shade of a large oak tree, I hardly believed my ears.

"You god-dammed niggers . . . go back to Africa!" he exploded, fury igniting in his deep blue eyes riveted on the two dark-skinned men in the audience who had dared to heckle the speaker.

He waved an aggressive, dismissive hand: "Go back to the jungle!"

An uproar that instantly swept the audience faded just as quickly.

Grinning defiance, the two hecklers raised their middle fingers at the speaker.

Slit-eyed, his face frozen with rage, the rabble-rouser bellowed, "We need to deport all these flipping people back to Africa! These savage animals have destroyed our beloved white countries!"

His accent was distinctly American, a southern drawl.

I stood there in the midst of the crowd, caught between amusement and alarm – amused because at Speakers' Corner almost everything tickled me; alarmed, because I couldn't reconcile the messenger, preaching from his altar of a wooden soap-box, with the message that he preached. It was like watching Martin Luther King advocating hatred and scorn.

The tall late-middle-aged, blue-eyed blond

man, wearing a well-tailored, navy-blue three-piece suit, looked the part of the quintessential gentleman.

"According to your Constitution all men are created equal!" a female London accent hollered from the thick of the crowd.

"A flipping lie!" the speaker protested, vehemently, holding up a medium sized book. "Check your Bible!"

"This thing called the American Constitution," he continued, "has been abused by our enemies – the Jews – in their attempts to dilute our pure white blood. They use it to promote the mongrelisation of the white race, the sinful race-mixing that is going on today!"

A few in the audience had begun to shout, "No! No!"

Calmly, the speaker waited for the booing and jeering to subside.

A dozen or so people wandered across, settling into the back of the crowd that had by then swelled to a small multitude.

His blue eyes probing the audience, the ranter went on, his tone unyielding. "The Founding Fathers got it wrong! They made a terrible mistake to include this blatant lie about the equality of man in the Declaration of Independence! These noble men, unfortunately, were fooled by the Jewish propaganda of liberty, equality and fraternity they were spreading all over Europe!"

The American lifted his voice over the uproar

that broke loose. "Check the White Man's Bible for yourself!"

"The what?" someone shouted.

"The White Man's Bible!" The ranter boomed. "This one!"

He held the book before him like a sacred offering, adding, "Read it, and learn the truth about the inferiority of the mud races, and the superiority of our whiteness!"

Muffled conversations sprang up across the audience.

"Go back to America, you bloody racist!" a light-skinned man with short spiky black hair rebuked from the back of the burgeoning crowd.

"At least back in the States they wear a hood," an un-attractive white woman standing next to me whispered.

"Yeah . . . . the Ku Klux Klan," I muttered.

The man carried on bombastically, unperturbed, his gaze shifting over the crowd. "The stupidity of the founding fathers led them to include in the Declaration of Independence the phrase that all men are created equal. A flipping error that continues to plague us to this very day! History and nature tells us differently. This phrase is the foundation of the Jewish strategy to dilute the white race."

I listened in stunned disbelief, my senses of sight and of hearing still fighting the battle over the bizarre disparity between message and messenger.

"This was their sacred belief . . . you bigot!" a male American accent shouted.

"Nonsense!" the speaker snapped, dabbing his temples with a white handkerchief. "The founding fathers didn't believe in racial equality!"

Waiting for the babble sweeping the audience to ebb away, his eyes surveyed the congregation, his gaze intense.

Then he bellowed. "How could they have believed in equality when they themselves owned plantations and thousands of slaves? . . . Slaves that they bought and sold like chattels, like animals!"

For a split second total silence ensued, until a young white man standing next to me shattered it: "Bollocks!"

He glanced across at me, sympathy flickering in his eyes. I shrugged, sending him a weak smile.

But I knew the speaker had a point – in fact, he was spot on. The founding fathers of America had themselves been owners of slaves. Indeed, it was widely alleged that Thomas Jefferson, third President of the United States and one of the authors of the Declaration of Independence, had fathered several children with a slave named Sally Hemmings.

Pompously, the American continued: "Surely they could not believe these slaves were equal to themselves! Under pressure from the Jews, they made an error. As simple as that! The founding fathers were convinced of the inferiority of the slaves. They thought they were doing the Jews a favour – not the Negroes!"

No one heckled.

I glanced around me. The crowd had grown thicker, still growing steadily. Still not a word of protest.

His voice rolling with the lilt of the deep American South, the speaker went on: "If the founding fathers intended to create equality for the black folks, why then did they continue to regard them as chattels when they later wrote the American Constitution!"

"That's a bloody lie!" a voice bellowed in my ear.

I too felt like shouting, but restrained myself.

"Check it for yourselves," the Southern drawl continued. "If they considered them equal, why did they not give the Negroes a vote? Why were they not given citizenship? Why were they not allowed to participate in government? Why were they not given any civil rights? Where is the equality?"

A momentary silence fell over the audience.

The speaker paused, studying his congregation with slitted eyes.

"Women didn't have the vote, either!" a female Birmingham accent shouted.

"Exactly!" The blond man retorted. "Women did not have the vote because they weren't considered equal to men! That proves my point!"

I awaited the rebuttal. None came.

"There was nothing in the American Constitution for the blacks!" He continued, sounding triumphant now. "The closest thing for them was that their masters were given additional votes in determining the number of congressmen to be allotted to each state."

After a brief pause, he spouted, "What equality! The founding fathers made a mistake; they never believed in equality for the Negroes!"

As if for effect, he then paused for several long seconds, studying the sea of faces before him.

No one spoke. No one heckled. I surveyed the faces around me; I saw faces quiet, in contemplation.

"Now everyone is talking the same crap of all men being created equal . . ."

A roar of disapproval met those words.

"Racist pig!" a dark-skinned man, with short, kinky dreadlocks called over his shoulder as he stormed off.

The Southern gentleman was still speaking. "Think of any TV commercial you can remember!"

He paused.

Then the words ripped from his throat. "There is always a flipping Negro taking centre stage! When was the last time you saw an all-white TV commercial? Why is that so?"

Muffled conversations sprang up amid the booing and jeering. Well past the point of irritation, I groaned, but captivated, I remained rooted to the spot.

The speaker took a breather, studying the range of expressions before him.

A few metres away, in Park Lane, I glimpsed a

big red double-decker bus; I was reminded that this was London, not some little state in the Deep South of the United States in the 1950s. A wry smile stretched my lips.

The disclaimer's voice cut through my thoughts. "There is a conspiracy! Can't you see? Do you really believe it's goods they are really advertising?"

"No – your Mum!" shouted a male voice on the outskirts, his attempt at humour falling flat on its face.

"They're promoting the mongrelisation of our race!" The blond man paused. "All this race-mixing crap! And the sad thing is that our young white people, being impressionable and easily fooled, are beginning to believe the propaganda that mixing is the right and natural thing for them."

Another uproar.

The speaker's voice thundered through: "I've been here for three days, and everywhere I turn, mixed-race couples – everywhere! You Londoners don't know what the hell you're doing! I've been to every major city in the world, and London is the worst I have seen. This is disgusting!"

A spontaneous cheer swept the defiant crowd, as if the words were a compliment deserving of a standing ovation.

The speaker frowned, his eyebrows arched.

"My white brethren," he pleaded, "We must work together to stop our young from mixing . . ."

"Once you go black, you never go back!" a jerry-curled black man standing in front of me shouted rhythmically.

Hoots rose up from a small group of young black men in the midst of the crowd.

The speaker started to say something, then stopped. A moment later, as though some private thought had just entered his head, he slitted his mouth into a smile. Again, I saw the perfect aristocratic gentleman. Never judge a book by its cover, I had learned.

I whispered the words of the Bob Marley song that came to mind, 'The biggest man you ever did see, was once a baby'.

I found myself wondering what the speaker would have been like as a child.

His smile still lingering, the speaker continued, "We must give it to them, they're a smart bunch. The Jews are pushing the whites and the Negroes to mix, while they do all in their powers to keep their own blood pure. Their press, their synagogues and all their organizations are warning their people against inter-racial marriages, against inter-faith marriages. They're even trying to discourage their people from marrying whites! We are now below them! In Israel, anyone not born of a Jewish mother is a goy, a non-Jew, an outsider, and can't be married or buried in Israel, nor can they become a citizen or enjoy any of the other civil rights of a person born Jewish. Racial solidarity is the order of the day, whether a Jew lives in Israel or anywhere else in the world!"

After the commotion had ebbed away, the blond man pointed to a lanky, bearded, middle-aged white man with a modest handle-bar moustache, standing to his left. "I want to introduce you to one of our disciples, who will provide further enlightenment, by reading a chapter from our Bible."

Whispered conversations again swept the audience.

I thought the time was ripe to make my exit, but curiosity got the better of me.

The poker-faced man, attired in a tweed jacket over faded black jeans, stepped onto the soap-box, and skipping all preamble, proclaimed, "We must reclaim our land!"

This time it was laughter that rippled through the crowd.

"What land?" a gruff male voice bellowed.

His eyes never leaving the pages of the slender book, the unsmiling, ancient-looking man flipped through its pages, stopping somewhere in the middle. He began to read, his voice almost prophetic with threat.

"Land belongs to those people that were strong enough to conquer it and hold it. This is the basic law of history and of Nature, and always will be."

A noisy wave of dissent swept the sprawling crowd.

The bespectacled 'disciple' read on, his voice raised above the rancour.

"The Jews themselves drove one and a half million Arabs from their homelands in Palestine, and drove them out into a dry, hot, barren desert to starve or die of thirst. This was Arab homeland that their ancestors had lived on for 2,000 years. The United States helped the Jews do it, and cheered them on with our aid when this atrocity was committed. Where were all the goddamned bleeding hearts then?"

The words hit silence. No one spoke. No one jeered. Everyone listened now . . . attentively.

The first speaker slitted his mouth into a smile. The reader continued, still unsmiling, his eyes sparkling with contentment.

"'Taking the Jewish–Christian bible at face value, we find in the Old Testament that the Jews drove the Philistines, the Hittites, the Canaanites, out of Palestine and took over their land, and God goaded them on to do so. So God morally condones such conduct!'"

Uproar broke loose.

"No! No! No!"

"Rot in hell!"

"This is blasphemous!"

I too had heard enough.

The sun was retreating behind a cluster of dark clouds when, deep in thought, I turned on my heel and headed for my bus stop.

Twenty minutes later I was making my way home on Bus Number Thirty-Six, conflicting emotions playing in my mind. On the one hand, I had seen an impeccably clad individual – an educated-sounding white man at that – stand before an audience and deliver the most venomous racial filth I'd ever heard. Somehow, my colonial upbringing, despite the known brutality of slavery, had programmed deep within my subconscious – and that of generations of West Indians – the notion that the white man was nothing but gentle, courteous, God-fearing, kind, wise, and unlikely to hurt even a fly. Unlike African Americans, who continue to endure the harsh realities of racial prejudice, my generation of West Indians had hardly seen the white man in roles other than those in which he displayed only those noble qualities in the roles of doctor, governor, evangelist, priest, diplomat, expatriate bank manager. Few exceptions.

As I glanced across to an attractive half-caste girl who had just boarded the bus at Westminster Bridge, a long-forgotten memory surfaced in my mind. When a twelve-year-old, mentally challenged black girl who daily lounged around the Catholic presbytery in LaClery gave birth to a baby boy the spitting image of the Irish parish priest, many parishioners vehemently declared that never would the white priest do something like that . . . he would never 'interfere with' the retarded child. It apparently made no difference to them that the Pontiff's representative was the only white man in the community, and that the baby was clearly only half black.

What I witnessed at Speakers' Corner today had instantly reprogrammed the chip that colonialism had so surreptitiously implanted within me.

The chip that had me believing that all white

people are good, respectable, God-fearing, law abiding citizens, wanting the best for all society, for all humanity.

And as I sat there on the top deck, deep in thought, the realization hit me that, whether they knew it or not, people subject to a colonial upbringing carried around these chips, chips that trigger their insecurities, altering their behaviour, once finding themselves in the presence of those who reminded them of their former masters. Only, colonialism has long since died but no one has bothered to do the reprogramming in the minds of victims. So it becomes a task each individual must do for himself. Today, at Speakers' Corner, I'd completed my reprogramming.

At the same time, the vehement refusal of the predominantly white crowd to buy the American's racist dissertation had given me a new-found respect for London and for Londoners. Though I'd never visited any other big city, I could imagine no other place that would so aptly embody such a wholesome combination of freedom of speech and racial harmony.

From that day, London loomed large in my mind.

But as Bus Number Thirty-Six sped past New Cross on its way to Lewisham, I knew I had to relegate all these philosophical musings to the back of my mind. I needed to clear my mind to ready myself for tomorrow's date with my arch-enemy, that horrid contraption called The Computer.

CHAPTER 19

A summer that I had prayed would never end was fast fading into a mere memory. All over London, trees blazed in brilliant reds, oranges, yellows, browns, and golds. Magnificent leaves fluttered on branches, preparing for the twirling cascade down to the waiting ground.

That crisp but bright autumn morning, in the vicinity of Liverpool Street, I stood before the impressive rectangular building of steel and bluish glass. My eyes climbed the reflective glass panes several storeys up above, shimmering in the early morning sun, casting a tower of light towards the heavens. I felt confident that with my leather briefcase, brand new double-breasted business suit, and sporting a slick jerry-curl, that I blended in with the city professionals striding briskly up and down the street.

A pigeon flew down to the pavement at my feet. It began pecking at a discarded kebab shell, its purple neck sparkling iridescent in the stark sunlight. A sure sign of good luck, I mused.

As I approached the grand entrance, the automatic revolving doors spun noiselessly into an exquisitely furnished marble reception. An attractive young lady in a black jacket over a lilac blouse sat behind an oval-shaped granite counter. She offered visitors smiles and pleasantries. Standing to attention at the far right of the reception area, a uniformed sentinel offered a stern face and stark indifference.

Within a few nervous minutes of announcing my arrival to the receptionist, I saw a conservatively dressed middle-aged lady coming down to meet me. I rose to greet her, shaking her outstretched hand. She introduced herself, flashing a smile that instantly disappeared, then led me briskly across the carpeted floor to an ultra-modern elevator with glistening brass panels and mirrored walls.

Not thirty seconds later, I heard a ping! as the elevator doors slid open into a spacious open area divided into row upon row of cubicles. The place was buzzing with animated talk. As we strode down a floor thickly carpeted in a soft blue, I glanced across at individuals seated at the interlocking desks, with low dividers separating them, talking animatedly into headsets, and other workers tapping away furiously on keyboards . . . keyboards attached to computers. Most were young men in their early- to mid-twenties, clad in designer suits and fashionable silk ties. Here and there, yet more designer jackets draped the backs of high-back swivel chairs, their owners sporting black suspenders over colourfully striped long-sleeved shirts.

Midway across the floor was an attractive petite young lady who strode by confidently in an inch-perfect black business suit with the skirt falling to just above the knee, her large sparkling brown eyes barely registering my presence. I marvelled at her resemblance to the girl of my dreams. The slender frame; the dignified, vertical posture; the long jet-black curly hair that flowed over her shoulders; the slightly upturned nose – a white version of Susanna, I thought, smiling inwardly.

As I swaggered a pace or two behind my hostess, my eyes tracked the young woman's every move-ment as she swished by like a warm breeze, heading towards the far end of the floor. She took her seat at the wood-grained desk and flicked me a specu-lative sideways glance. I thought I detected a hint of a smile at the corners of her mouth.

I flashed her a smile.

"Mr Gurley!" the middle-aged matronly woman called out – not for the first time, I suspected.

I quickly turned around, my face reddening with embarrassment.

"Your meeting's through here," she said, un-smiling, as she motioned me to a glass-walled office towards the back of the floor.

I took a seat on a black swivel chair in front of a wood-grained desk. Before I had time to look about me, a pleasant-faced, bespectacled, short, dapper man stepped through the door. Smiling, he reached his right hand forward. I rose to shake hands with the gentleman, who seemed to be pushing his mid-thirties, and had a well-groomed crop of shiny jet-black hair. He introduced himself as the financial accountant, before taking a seat across from me.

"Thank you for coming at such short notice," he said, in a deep, cultured voice, his pale blue eyes studying me closely.

"Happy to assist," I said, flicking a glance at the glowing computer screen on the side desk.

"To be frank," he said, smiling weakly, "we have a bit of a problem that we need to sort out, like, yesterday. And I should tell you that we've already had two other temps from a different agency trying to sort this out, and they've got nowhere."

I nodded, noncommittal, sitting back, my left foot propped on my right knee.

"With our interim audit due to start next month," the accountant continued, raking a pale hand through his hair, "we need to get our house in order . . . we can't afford to take any chances."

"Sure," I nodded. "What exactly is the problem?" I asked, striving for a professional tone of voice.

Tapping his bare chin with the top of his Mont Blanc pen, the accountant said casually, "Our portfolios ledger is off by 1.8 million pounds . . . it's just not reconciling."

A chill raked through my flesh.

I needed a minute or two for my mind to register what my ears had just heard.

His blue eyes studied my face, seemingly trying to read my reaction.

When the words finally registered, I drew a deep but silent breath, willing my voice to keep steady. "Sorry, what did you say?"

"Our portfolios ledger has a huge difference . . . it refuses to balance . . . it is out by 1.8 million pounds."

"I see," I said, not seeing at all.

"Yes, it's a bloody mess."

I ventured a question to break the ensuing silence. "So what is the exact figure?"

"1.8 million pounds."

I realized I'd been holding my breath. I exhaled. "Exactly 1.8 million pounds?" I asked.

"Exactly."

My confidence leaped. This could only mean one thing. I felt the warm glow of an adrenalin rush.

"That shouldn't be too difficult to find, then," I said after a moment's hesitation, maintaining a straight face.

I could see scepticism growing on the accountant's face.

"Beg your pardon?"

"It sounds like a simple transposition error."

He squinted at me doubtfully. "A what?"

"A transposition error."

A vacant stare greeted me.

I was surprised that he, a qualified accountant, hadn't heard of the elementary accounting phenomenon. I was also surprised that I found myself revelling in his ignorance.

The adrenalin was now racing through me.

"The difference you're looking for is exactly divisible by nine, so, all things being equal, it is more than likely a transposition error."

My client didn't respond, but I could see his face changing, growing darker around the eyes. After a moment he cocked his head looking sheepishly at me. He didn't understand . . . his face showed it.

I delighted in explaining to the cynical accountant that when figures are transposed – placed back to front or vice versa – an error or difference exactly divisible by nine results. I illustrated the example of 28 being switched to 82, resulting in a difference of 54 – divisible by nine, with no decimal portion in the answer.

Frowning, the accountant dug into his breast pocket, whipped out a scientific calculator, and for the next few seconds tapped away feverishly at the tiny keys. Then he stopped abruptly and gave me a stupefied stare, as though he had just discovered that the earth was really flat.

It was my turn to look incredulous, but I didn't. I knew better.

But I'd long since learned that it was one thing to suspect the cause of an accounting error and quite another to actually find it. Hence, two days later, three giant computer printouts, bound in a shiny, blue, plastic cover, still lay one atop the other at my feet. Another two printouts sprawled over the surface of my desk.

A side-table at my right bore the weight of a dot-matrix Epson printer that sat next to the glowing computer screen displaying rows and columns of tiny green figures. Behind closed doors in the small glass-walled office, with intense focus, my eyes jerked from one printout to another, then to the flickering screen, and back to the large printouts, again, and again. Ever so often, my index fingers hovered over the keyboard, jabbing keys, the screen responding, scrolling up, down, across.

I had come a long way since that first, failed, assignment six months before.

Countless days and evenings at the Lewisham Central Library ploughing through volumes of computer books, had given me a start, a basic theoretical understanding of the machines that had once floored me. But it was my two-week voluntary stint at a local council that had provided the final conquest. Like a kid with a brand-new toy, I'd played incessantly with the standalone IBM PC seemingly abandoned at the back of the office. My once arch-enemy, defeated, had become my loyal subject, and, placed in my service, a tool of my trade.

My new-found skills, however basic, had propelled me back onto the contract accounting scene. Reed Accountancy had welcomed me back, like the Prodigal Son, with wide-open arms. Securing some attractive short-term placements with City clients, I was able to sharpen my computer skills, becoming proficient in spreadsheets – VisiCalc, MultiPlan – and word processors – WordPerfect, WordStar.

But London wasn't, for me, all work and no play. With my two newest and closest friends, Jamaicans, Alastair, a law student, and Carris, an accounting student, I had become a regular on the capital's night scene. Hardly a weekend passed without some solid clubbing. And it certainly helped me socially that I had left the Lewisham bed-sit and now shared a flat in Kidbrook, also near Greenwich, with a St. Lucian friend.

Now, as my pencil encircled a suspicious figure at the top right corner of the large page in front of me, a muffled ring, emanating from somewhere on my cluttered desk, startled me.

My mind a flurry of figures, I reached out beneath the blue plastic cover, and picked up the phone.

"Hello."

"Hello? Is this Rudy?" a cut-glass female English accent asked.

"Yes, it is," I breathed, my eyes glued to the faint numbers across the large printout. "Who's calling?"

"Oh, hi, Rudy. I'm really happy that I'm finally able to reach you." I sensed a happy, smiling face at the other end of the line, but figures, none divisible by nine, continued to swirl around in my head.

"My name is Lana; I'm calling from Accountancy Staff Ltd."

I frowned, slightly confused, wondering why on earth, after registering with this agency several months before, they had only now decided to call.

"Okay," I said into the phone.

"I hope I'm not interrupting," the smiling voice continued, "but I finally got hold of your number from one of our sources. We've heard some very positive things about you, Rudy. Obviously, you are an excellent accountant, and you have made quite a name for yourself on the temp scene in London."

I thanked her for her kind words, but my eyes rolled cynically, suspecting the caller had merely stumbled upon my name in one of her old files.

"As I'm sure you're aware, Rudy, Big Bang has really buoyed up the market for contract accountants such as yourself, and I'm pleased to tell you that we have a number of positions that are ideally suited to a candidate of your calibre. I was wondering if you had a moment or so to pop round our offices at Holborn to discuss some of these exciting opportunities."

While I wasn't contractually tied to my agent, I put a value on loyalty. "I'd be happy to, but I'm a little busy at the moment."

"I very much appreciate that." She hesitated a moment. "Big Bang is a very exciting opportunity for everyone, and we would really like to have you on our team."

She spoke again after another brief pause. "And of course, we will be unveiling our new bonus scheme which is second to none."

Desperate to return to the suspicious figure on the page in front of me, I said, "Can I call you a bit later . . . sometime . . . tomorrow perhaps? I'm in the middle of trying to crack a reconciliation."

After she'd given me her telephone number at least three times, we hung up. No doubt the polished accent had sensed my reticence, and I'd sensed her disappointment. But this wasn't my problem. I had just one problem. A big problem. I needed to find a 1.8-million-pound error. My credibility was on the line.

Pushing the telephone across the desk away from the printouts, I sat back, deep in thought, my right index finger caressing my temple. I hadn't given as much thought as perhaps I should have to the recent shock wave hitting the City of London.

On 27th October 1986, less than a month ago, Big Bang had rocked the City. Thatcher's Conservative government had struck a deadly blow to Britain's Wall Street, transforming it virtually overnight. No longer would the affairs of the City be run like those of a gentleman's club where most brokers knew and trusted each other, where bargains could be made by word of mouth, where standards of integrity were self-imposed, where outsiders were kept out. Competition was now the order of the day. Established stockbroking firms now had to put up with the onslaught of American, Japanese, and Canadian firms, with more aggressive attitudes, more modern methods, and probably more resources. Not such good news for the established

London brokers; excellent news for young professionals – young professionals like me, even though I was just eighteen months out of the Caribbean.

The next day – after I'd found the error, and after the accountant had asked me to stay on to assist with the interim audit – the telephone again disturbed my train of thought. It was my agent. Her message was similar to her competitor's: Big Bang, exciting opportunities, more money. But she did also tell me about a more pressing engagement; she'd booked me to attend an interview the following day.

When I explained my reluctance to leave my current assignment – without, of course, mentioning Susanna's lookalike – my agent pointed out that I was contracted only until the firm's year-end, next month, so I would have more than enough time to complete my current job.

Bright and early next morning, I found myself at a nondescript building at the Old Bailey. In an unpretentious, tobacco-scented office, I sat across a cluttered desk from the English finance director of a firm of Canadian stockbrokers.

Attired in an old-fashioned three-piece suit, and aged, I imagined, in his mid-fifties, this bespectacled Englishman with thinning auburn hair and a pipe wedged firmly in the corner of his mouth smiled broadly as he studied the CV on the desk before him.

"So," he said, pushing out his lower lip and nodding slowly, the pipe dangling from his lips, eyes riveted on the folder in front of him, "You have impressive references, I see."

His eyes shifted to my face, as if trying to match the written details with the person before him. Frowning slightly, he returned his gaze to the pages in front of him.

"You've also had some impressive assignments along the way." He nodded, as if to himself. "And made a very good impression." This time his gaze met mine, and we shared a smile.

"I have been fortunate in my contracts thus far."

The pipe wobbled in his mouth as he nodded, listlessly. "Yes . . . yes . . . I'm sure you have."

"Here's the thing," he said, in a preliminary sort of way, closing the file and leaning over the desk towards me, speaking in a hushed tone, his coffee breath now in my face. "We're a new company here in London, and we have a very exciting opportunity to expand in leaps and bounds." He eyes studied my face as if expecting a reaction.

I nodded, but decided to hold my tongue.

"What we are really after is a bright young chap, such as yourself, to take a permanent position within our accounts team."

That caught me completely off-guard. "Permanent? I said, "I . . . I was under the impression this was an interview for a temporary position, like my other assignments."

"Yes, absolutely," said the Englishman, a devilish

smile appearing as he leaned back in his high-back swivel chair, his voice now an octave lower. "We haven't yet sorted out the terms, but I can assure you that it will be quite favourable, just the right sort of stepping stone for a budding accountant such as yourself."

"Well, I . . ."

"Yes, yes," his voice cut through dismissively, the pipe firmly wedged between his teeth. "I am sure this was not what you were expecting, but I urge you to consider the benefits. At this stage in your career you will do well with some solid permanent experience under your belt. Remaining a temp for too long could be rather detrimental to your career, you know."

He gazed at me for several seconds, took a puff of his pipe, then blew out the swirling, sweet-scented smoke. "Young man, I give you my assurance that I will personally see to it that your duties are many and varied within the accounts department, so that you do develop into a well-rounded accountant, which will undoubtedly do your career good."

"I understand. But I have other obligations, particularly to my studies, that make contract work more convenient to me."

"Mmmm." He gripped his pipe more firmly, his teeth clicking against the stem. "Your studies are not incompatible with the position I'm offering you here, and we would, as I said, make the offer more than attractive. Rest assured, Rudy, that we will fully support your endeavours to become qualified; not only will we finance your books and exam fees, but you can also look forward to some generous study leave before your exams."

He paused a moment, then added, "As a chartered accountant myself, I do understand the importance of becoming qualified, you know."

Silence hung for a taut moment as my mind tried to frame an appropriate response. I found myself warming to the proposal, but a little voice in my head told me I was playing with forbidden fruit.

"Tell you what," the finance director said, conclusively, "Go away, think about it, and get back to me once you have seen our offer. You should receive something in the mail on Thursday."

He stuck a hairy hand out across the desk; I reached out and shook it. "Thank you. Okay, I will."

As I strode out of the office, my mind was a whirl of opposing thoughts. Oddly, I felt apprehensive, yet excited at the prospect of a permanent job.

I needed to revisit my game plan.

I found sleep difficult that night as I lay in bed taking stock of my life.

Half an hour later, I was smiling as I rolled over onto my side. I'd concluded that everything had gone like clockwork thus far. I'd passed all my papers at first sitting, I'd acquired some solid accounting experience – I was well and truly on my way.

But I shuddered at the thought of a permanent

job – an entirely different ball game. My life as a temp met all my requirements: flexibility, flexibility, flexibility.

"Nothing should get in the way of my studies . . . nothing," I whispered emphatically, as I checked the little red clock on my side table. Eleven fifteen.

I called to mind the other reasons why I found contract work so attractive. It allowed me to develop new skills providing access to the latest software and accounting systems; it offered a variety of projects in differing environments, an excellent way to develop and enhance personal skills, communicate with people from different backgrounds, and learn new ways of working through different businesses, industries and cultures. That's exactly what I needed to equip myself properly for the role that I knew awaited me back home.

The minor matter of a rate of seven pounds an hour, though – considerably better than I'd expected – wasn't altogether irrelevant.

Flipping my pillow over and mashing it into shape, I recalled the conversation with my agent earlier today. She hadn't been totally over the moon about the prospect of losing my services. Apparently, she too had been led to believe the client was only interested in a temporary placement.

"It's your call," she'd told me, "but you have to look at it from all angles before you make your decision. Don't let yourself be tempted by a big salary. After all you are still studying. Remember you told me that this was your top priority."

I had taken my agent's advice with a pinch of salt, aware that she ran the risk of losing a good source of recurring revenue.

I checked the clock on my side table. It had just gone past one. I needed to call it quits, but my mind insisted on returning to my present, not altogether pitiable, predicament. The extra money would help. I might possibly be able to fit my studies around a permanent job.

Two days later, I received the letter of offer from the firm of Canadian brokers.

The next day I wrote back . . . I had just one question that lingered unanswered: when could I start?

CHAPTER 20

In the wake of Big Bang the City seemed ensnared in the throes of a feeding frenzy. Dynamic, fast-talking Americans and Canadians, and the more apparently humble but intensely focused Japanese, had invaded. Hundreds of companies had sprung up all over London, entrepreneurs sensing the opportunity to make a killing, sometimes by pushing the edges of the envelope.

Increasingly, reports appeared in the press about shoddy, unscrupulous, vice-prone companies roaming the City. These 'cowboys', it was reported, were proving difficult both to identify and to regulate.

Still relatively fresh out of the Caribbean, with my own narrow focus, I cared little initially about the happenings in the financial district of London. But finding myself caught up in the midst of it all, I realized I'd got every reason to care.

I had a nagging suspicion I'd found myself in one of those 'cowboy' outfits when I took up employment at the firm of Canadian brokers. All my instincts told me so. To begin with, I found myself running an accounting system that seemed geared only towards feeding the CEO the bank balance whenever he passed my desk the five or six times that he did so hourly. It also caused me grave concern that I could find no system that recorded, monitored, or tracked which investors were investing in which securities.

From a makeshift, no-frills 'cubicle-farm' in the back of the nondescript brick building, sweet-talking salesmen in designer suits seduced ordinary citizens, mainly pensioners, into parting with their life savings. In return, investors received a piece of paper laying claim to a slice of one of two companies that had allegedly discovered diamond deposits somewhere in South America. The so-called prospectus, designed to give would-be investors sufficient information to guide their investment decision, seemed to me merely a glossy brochure, presenting only scant details on the companies' operations.

But my main concern remained that nowhere could I find a system that administered investor information. As far as I could see, these poor souls mailed in their cheques, and in return received their share certificate; from there the process seemed to come to a grinding halt.

A crucial step was missing.

From my Company Law studies I had learned of the requirement for companies to maintain a share register, recording the names and addresses of shareholders, and the number and class of share held by each; otherwise, there can be no way of identifying individual shareholders for purposes of dividend payment, share transfers, and so on.

My employers appeared to be in breach of this fundamental requirement. They seemed interested only in the cheques they so promptly banked. Add to this the wild rumours that neither of the two companies the brokers promoted really existed, and you had the makings of an entire Western movie full of cowboys.

My nagging suspicion persisted, growing stronger as the days passed.

And it was on the morning of 6th February 1987 – two months into the job – that I took the short walk that seemed a mile to the finance director's office, and with little preamble, handed him my letter of resignation.

Much to my relief, the pipe-smoking Englishman seemed neither terribly surprised nor disappointed when he read the note that took immediate effect. He, too, the finance director admitted, was contemplating his own departure.

"Big Bang," he said sombrely, head bowed, "has brought too many cowboys into London."

"Professionals like us," he added after a thoughtful pause, the pipe dangling from his mouth, "ought not to be associated with outfits such as these."

I nodded agreement.

He was silent for several long seconds, then, sympathy flickering in his eyes, he glanced up at me. "Young man, I believe you've made the right decision for your career, and I applaud you for that."

Within a day or two I was merrily back in the temp accounting scene. It was two or three weeks later that word reached me that the authorities had moved in and shut down my former employer. Talk abounded that the Canadian CEO had absconded. I received not a word of what had become of my former boss, the pipe-smoking Englishman.

But bizarre as that experience was, it paled in comparison to what happened on 19th October 1987.

That was the day the stock market crashed. Black Monday.

Mysteriously, the US Dow Jones Industrial Average fell twenty two point six per cent, the largest one-day decline in recorded stock-market history. Then, like a pack of cards, one by one, stock markets around the world collapsed: Tokyo, Hong Kong, Singapore, Australia, London. Investors lost millions . . . instantly.

My own modest portfolio of one thousand, five hundred pounds, plummeted to five hundred pounds. A devastating loss.

Over the next few months, I watched in horror as the world around me crumbled. All over London, almost daily, entire floors of workers received their marching orders. Being 'down-sized' became the number one fear among young professionals.

The yuppies, the so-called young urban professionals, became an endangered species, teetering on the brink of extinction. It became apparent that many had expected their earnings to continue to grow unabated, and had run up staggering credit-card bills. Thus, they suffered an affliction that bankers called 'Yuppie Bill Syndrome'.

By the dozens, BMW's were being returned to showrooms. All over the country 'Yuppie pawn-shops' were opening up. These upscale establishments allowed the young professionals to cash in their more expensive toys to meet their living expenses. Paraphernalia: Rolex watches, designer suits and mobile phones that had defined a generation were now being cashed in for a fraction of their original value. Non-work suits fell out of chic, as ripped jeans and tee-shirts replaced the designer names of only a few weeks previous. Thus, the style 'Downscale Chic' was born.

Many of the former Young Urban Professionals, now renamed Young Unhappy Professionals, dropped out of the fast lane and sought a simpler, stress-free existence, many relocating to the countryside. Others changed focus altogether, moving into charitable work: environmental protection, fighting cancer, aid for Africa.

The social transformation that unfolded right before my eyes utterly dumbfounded me. In a matter of months, I had seen the redefinition of an entire generation. I watched in wonder, trying to learn from the experience.

As the months rolled by, the City regained some calm. My modest portfolio recovered fifteen per cent of its original value. Life began to get back to normal for those who'd survived the crash; fortunates like me who, unlike many of my colleagues, had remained employed throughout the ordeal.

Yet again, I found myself on the receiving end of a permanent job offer. A subsidiary of the Royal Bank of Scotland, where I'd remained as a contract accountant throughout the crash, offered me the position of assistant accountant, an offer I respectfully declined.

With a few more exams yet to take, I couldn't afford to lose focus on my studies. It was difficult enough studying on my own. Having seen how fickle the finance industry could be, I reminded myself never to lose sight of progressing towards full qualification.

The long-term implications of the crash worried me; downsized companies normally take months, if not years, to regroup. My options would be limited. For me, London would never be the same again.

CHAPTER 21

It was on 18th November 1987 that London suffered yet another catastrophe. A discarded match had set fire to rubbish and grease, which blazed up beneath wooden escalators at Kings Cross St. Pancras London underground station. The raging fire burnt out the top level of the station. Thirty one people perished that day.

Kings Cross was on my route. Daily, I traversed the underground station on my way to and from work at Wood Green. I might have been caught up in the calamity had I not, the week before, relocated to Milton Keynes.

The atmosphere in London hadn't been the same since the dramatic stock market crash. An ubiquitous gloom hung over the City. So, after turning down the offer of a permanent job, I thought the time was ripe for a change of scene.

Milton Keynes was rapidly becoming the industrial capital of England as companies availed themselves of generous relocation incentives. But it was also the efficient road network, availability of land for expansion, relatively low-cost housing and proximity to London that attracted investors. I'd been drawn to Milton Keynes not only by my family's presence but also by the potential tranquillity the town offered after the hustle and bustle of the big city.

In London, my friends had called me a 'Buppie' – a Black Urban Professional; but I, like the soul-searching yuppies, craved a simpler existence.

I'd telephoned my brother, Simon, who was all too happy to rent me a room at his spacious three-bed council house he shared with his Scottish girlfriend and their baby daughter. I was happy to split the running expenses down the middle.

Rosemary, by then, had become lonely again. The year before, her husband had passed on.

Reed Accountancy had done the usual trick. They had put me in touch with their Milton Keynes office, and within a day or two I was back on the temp accounting scene.

Now, nine months later, in the medium-sized carpeted office, I sat at a circular table across from a tall, slender, Englishman with dark eyes and a mop of black hair just starting to turn grey. Smartly attired in a single-breasted navy-blue business suit, the man, in his mid-thirties, struck me as intelligent, articulate, and witty. He peered over his wire-rimmed spectacles as he spoke, seeming to use the lenses only to read from the CV on the table before him.

The hour-long interview had gone well. Our body language suggested it was time to wrap up.

I brought the tips of my fingers delicately together and looked at the Englishman over them with an expression of appreciation. "Thank you very much for attending and for being on time. I really do appreciate it. Clearly, as I am sure you're aware, the role of Accounts Payable Supervisor is an important one, and I do have several other candidates to interview. However, we should get back to you by the end of the week. Good luck. All the best."

Permitting myself a slight smile, I rose and offered an extended hand across the table.

"Thank you very much, sir, for the opportunity," said the Englishman, smiling modestly as he reached out for my hand across the table.

"I do hope you select the best person for the job," he added.

"All the best," I repeated, smiling knowingly, for I believed I'd found my man. Though he was several years my senior, I had no doubt we would enjoy working together.

Briefcase in hand, the Englishman turned and headed toward the varnished door, looking more confident than he had at the start of the interview. As he closed the door softly behind him, his dark eyes would have fallen upon a gold and black plaque on the door that read:

RUDY GURLEY
MANAGEMENT ACCOUNTANT

I strode over to the executive desk at the back of my office. Taking a seat, I riffled through the stack of CVs on the desk before me. It had been a hectic day.

'Six down, one more to go,' I muttered to myself, as I turned to the computer on the side-table, and proceeded to update my Word Perfect file with my notes on the interview.

Fifteen minutes later, task completed, and feeling pleased with myself, I spun round in the high-back swivel chair to face the large tinted-glass panel. My eyes drifted out beyond the huge industrial buildings below to the grassy landscape in one of the several industrial parks that had sprung up in Milton Keynes. My gaze then glided to the parking lot below. My six-year old blue Talbot didn't look out of place parked next to the red Ford Escort – the Talbot was not the most fancy of cars, but it would have to do for now.

Then, as it often does during moments of repose, my mind drifted, mulling over recent events.

When I'd arrived in Milton Keynes, Reed Accountancy had placed me at a small manufacturing company that had required bank accounts reconciled and the general ledger cleaned out. At the end of my first month, the chief accountant had made an offer to me to stay on permanently, as his assistant.

This time I'd accepted, because my strategy had evolved. As a contract accountant over the past two and a half years, I'd acquired a wealth of solid accounting experience, but I increasingly felt the need to step up a notch to prepare better for the more formidable challenges future roles would pose. Management and decision-making skills were critical to my professional development. Permanent employment offered the best route to develop these.

From the start, I'd enjoyed good relations with my immediate boss, the chief accountant, an Indian man whose life revolved around his two pre-teen sons. Though in his mid-fifties, my boss looked much older.

I had often wondered whether Katan Patel was merely passing time before retirement, for it wasn't difficult to sense a lack of enthusiasm and vigour in the way he performed his duties. Not that I'd had any gripes about carrying the small finance department as my boss sat studiously at his desk, marking and preparing homework for his sons. Being thrown in at the deep end was something I relished; working with Katan Patel left me little option but to swim.

The chief executive, Mr. Harris, a self-made millionaire and owner of the business, had taken to consulting me directly on financial matters that were ordinarily the purview of the chief accountant. Nevertheless, I was a little taken aback when suddenly one day the silver-haired man had offered me my boss's job.

Loyalty had always been high on my agenda. Katan Patel, months from his fifty-sixth birthday, would find it difficult to land another job in a hurry. His two young sons were destined to attend Oxford, according to their father. He desperately needed to continue to build his financial resources to prepare for that eventuality.

Needless to say, I'd been under no illusion that I was anywhere near ready to assume the awesome weight of responsibility that came with the chief accountant's role. The top job required far more commitment, and offered a great deal less flexibility, than did my assistant accountant's role. So this could potentially damage any realistic hope I had of passing my finals. It was tough enough having to study while holding down a permanent job. Never a more ambitious man could one find, but nonetheless I firmly believed in mastering the art of walking before trying to run up steep hills.

"I'm thinking of looking for a more challenging role elsewhere," I'd told Katan the next day, having decided that leaving was my best option. I was merely four months into the job.

"I thought you liked it here?" Katan had replied, sounding not altogether displeased.

I'd looked away, deciding to keep the truth to myself. "Things here are not as I expected. Though I have learnt a great deal working with you."

Katan had taken a second or two before responding. "Okay . . . well . . . you need to do what is best for you; I won't stand in your way. I

248

will help you in any way I can . . . Actually I agree with you, prospects here are not that good at all. Obviously, don't worry about a reference . . . I will fix up something for you."

I'd smiled in gratitude and gone about my business, noting that my boss was already beginning to look years younger.

The next week, an unusually bright-eyed Katan had pointed to a vacancy in the local newspaper – the *Milton Keynes Citizen*. A medium-sized manufacturing company was seeking a management accountant – a step up from my then present position, but manageable nonetheless, I'd thought.

It was within two days of applying for the job that Katan had kindly driven me to the interview, along the way offering tips on interview techniques. Almost two hours later I'd emerged from the interview, having accepted the management accountant position. The job had come with a prestigious thirteen-thousand-pound annual salary, and help with books and exam fees was thrown in.

My boss had been delighted with the news, and even more so when I mentioned that I would have a large enough office, and a twenty-strong finance department, to manage.

Once settled in, I'd set about filling two vacancies within my department. The overwhelming response to the advertised jobs explained the pile of CVs now before me, on the leather-topped executive desk.

For the better part of this week, I had been

interviewing one candidate after another. At last, I'd seen someone with the sparkle in his eyes, the right qualifications, the right experience, the right attitude. I had a strong feeling that for the role of accounts payable supervisor, I'd found my man.

Now, as I sat back in my seat, feeling a smug satisfaction, my eyes surveyed the well-appointed, brightly lit, medium-sized office. Cream walls rose from graphite-grey tufted carpeting up to a suspended ceiling with recessed lights, contrasting against the brown wood decor.

Not bad, I smiled to myself. *Not bad at all. The little red boy from the Caribbean has done well . . . so far . . . not bad after three years!*

Basking in the warmth of that thought, for a fleeting moment, a mirage flashed before me, a vaguely recognizable scene. In that instant, it dawned upon me that my office was remarkably similar to the office I'd so often visualised on those cold, dreary nights, lying on the small bed in my Lewisham bed-sit. Years ago, in my mind's eye, I'd created a visual image of myself sitting in a brightly lit, well-furnished office, managing a team of professionals, making decisions, leading from the front. An image I visualized, morning, noon, and night, in quiet, peaceful moments.

Now it struck me like a lightning bolt that I'd already begun to live the dream – the dream that, years ago, I'd created in my mind; the dream that had sunk so deeply into my subconscious that I believed, with every fibre of my being, that it would one day materialise. It had already begun to do so.

Positive thinking notwithstanding, *Faith without works is dead*, the Bible said. To that end, I'd thrown all my energy into my job, and into my studies. I'd given it all that I had; every bit, nothing held back. My whole life had revolved around mastering my job and passing exams.

Now, rocking gently back and forth in my seat, I felt surfacing in my mind the memory of my temporary blindness that cold February morning in 1985.

I reached down for my briefcase and retrieved from it my little black book. I leafed through, settling on the page on which I'd written my resolutions on recovering my sight:

> *Gaining experience and passing exams are tasks of equal importance.*
>
> *I will find time for rest and relaxation – time for a social life. Pursuing a qualification should not mean that life is on hold, it is part of life's experience and I should savour the taste of this opportunity.*

But I doubted I'd remained true to the social aspects of my resolutions.

Despite many challenges and setbacks along the way I'd persevered. As always, I cringed when I recalled that first temporary assignment I'd so miserably failed at.

My landlord's words replayed in my mind:

"How could you . . . a little country boy from the Caribbean, hope to come to this white man's country and get a proper job with so many British people out of work? You know how long it take me to get to where I am today? Thirty years! . . . you must be crazy expecting to come here and make it in just a few months".

I smiled faintly, in acknowledgement of the irony that it was I who was now recruiting Brits.

Swivelling around in my seat, I gazed out upon the concrete structures in the distance, and at the unrelenting cold, grey sky up above. Something didn't feel quite right. For the past few months, a lingering doubt had been plaguing my soul, a matter of conscience.

For a moment my mind transported me back to St. Lucia. I saw my Aunt Sheila, at her Morne-du-Don home, her yellow cardigan falling over her baby-blue nightgown. She was in the kitchen cooking lunch as the roosters crowed; worried; wondering about me.

Why hasn't he written in four months? Will he return home as he's promised? Or will history repeat itself – will he follow in the footsteps of his mother and his father before him, and abandon his family? Is that why he's paid the student loan back so quickly?

I saw her, head bowed, walking slowly across the floor into the darkened living room, deep in thought. Then she was seating alone in the mono-chrome gloom of dawn, on the fluffy sofa, arms folded, leaning forward, thinking too much . . . worrying too much, about her nephew . . . her adopted son . . . me.

Then my mind strayed to a young lady . . . a young lady who hardly knew me . . . . a young lady about who, when first I'd laid eyes upon her, back in 1981, I'd made a personal vow: *she will one day* be *my wife.*

If only she had a clue of my intentions, or at least of my interest. Why had I stopped writing after just two letters way back in 1985?

I chastised myself. *How do you expect to marry this girl without keeping in touch with her? . . . Do you just expect to show up on her door step, out of the blue, one day?* I heard myself thinking. *Or could it be that you're flirting with the idea of making the UK your home for good, forgetting all and everything back home, could it be . . . ?*

The sound of the phone ringing on my desk yanked me back to the present. I picked it up. It was my former boss, Katan Patel. He wanted to meet me in the morning. We agreed on ten.

I checked my wall clock. It had just gone six. I decided on an early night . . . it was time to hit the road home.

When, the next day, the silver-haired, brown-skinned Indian man, with his loose, sagging face and drooping eyes, showed up at my office five minutes early, he seemed suitably impressed by his surroundings. I indicated the seats at the circular

253

table at the front of my office, arranged for coffee to be brought in, and sat across from my former boss who wore a tired brown lounge suit, his striped tie at half-mast around his neck.

"So, to what do I owe the pleasure?" I asked, as the attractive brunette with the pleasant smile closed the door behind her, having deposited two mugs of steaming black coffee on the table before us.

His eyes having followed the young lady's every movement, Katan flashed me a devilish smile, arching his bushy brows and nodding mischievously as though he'd just stumbled upon some little secret I'd concealed from him.

Uncertain what was on his mind, I chose the path of least resistance and returned the smile.

The smile that danced on his face now seemed almost obscene. "I'm happy to see how well you're doing, young man. I'm really proud of you. In fact I tell my sons about you all the time . . . I can only hope they grow up to be like you," he added, smiling, awaiting my response.

"Thanks . . . I learned a lot from you."

Katan seemed to go off into thought, and then he shook his head in a self-deprecating way. "Anyway," he said dismissively, "I just wanted to have a little chat with you . . . to offer you some advice."

I nodded, trying to conceal my utter surprise: "Okay."

Placing the mug carefully on its saucer, then

sliding it to one side, a serious look crossed his sagging face.

"You are aware that I think you are potentially a brilliant accountant . . . right?"

I nodded and didn't say anything.

Katan met my eyes and held them before going on. "I knew that from the very first day that I saw you on the job."

He lapsed into silence for several seconds. "I can see a very bright future ahead of you. In fact, as your career develops, I think you will find that you will go much farther than you originally expect."

"Thanks . . . you're very kind," I muttered.

"Not at all," Katan countered, fixing me with a firm stare. "It pays to speak the truth."

He seemed to hesitate a moment, his hands folded on his ample belly. Then he said, "At the risk of swelling your head, I'll go further and say that I can see that your future may very well not be restricted to accountancy. You will go much farther than that."

I put a question mark into my eyes. "Yeah? How so?"

"I believe you're destined to have teams of accountants working for you . . . I see you more as senior management material . . . a CEO or something like that . . . someone working at the highest level in the company . . . even at board level."

Katan paused and sipped his black coffee, glancing at me over large, thick-rimmed spectacles.

I was smiling inwardly at his words, as my mind

searched for an appropriate response. It found just one word: "Interesting."

"Now," Katan continued, more firmly, "I have been in this business a very, very long time, and the things I have learned you will never find in any of your text books."

He paused, gazing at me for several seconds. "I would like to share some of this with you."

"Thanks . . . I appreciate that."

"Not at all – it is I who should be grateful to you," he said, eyeing me warily, with a tired smile. His next few words caught me completely off guard.

"I know that Mr Harris offered you my job . . . I know why you left."

My face reddened, and grew hotter.

"And I sincerely appreciate what you did for me."

"Anyone would have done the same."

"No!" Katan fairly shouted. "No, they would not! And that's why I want to talk to you!"

I was a little taken aback. I didn't think the man had it in him to project his voice with such dynamism.

"Most people would have dug my grave and buried me alive . . . but you showed compassion, and I will never forget that. Compassion is a very rare quality these days, you know. People have become so selfish, they do not give a damn about anyone or anything but themselves."

Katan took an audibly deep breath, before continuing. "Rudy, you may find this hard to believe, but I was once a dynamic and enthusiastic young accountant, just like you." He smiled deprecatingly, adding, "I once had black hair!"

We both chuckled.

He seemed to go off into thought again, and then, speaking quietly, as if putting a wry confession through a screen to a priest, he said, "But people do make mistakes."

I watched the bags under his eyes sagging, as he added, "Not that it matters so much now. Now that I have my boys, nothing else matters. Whatever I do, I do for them."

I nodded, thoughtfully.

"Rudy, you have a lot of talent, charisma, and energy . . . and I like your enthusiasm and your determination to get things done quickly and professionally. But someone like you has to be very careful."

My eyebrows arched.

Katan opened his mouth to say something, but he apparently changed his mind.

I waited in silence.

Then he took a deep breath and asked, "Rudy, have you ever heard of Baltasar Gracian?

"Who?"

"Baltasar Gracian," he said slowly.

I shook my head. "No . . . never."

Katan smiled. "I'm not surprised, after all, the man died more than three hundred years ago. But anyway, he was probably one of the greatest philosophers of his time."

I nodded, impressed.

He reached for his black Filofax organiser on the table, and pulled out a small sheet of paper which he pushed across the table towards me. "Have a read."

I picked up the slip of paper and peered at the typed words:

Avoid outshining the master. All victory is odious but victory over the master, either part of stupidity, or of fate. Superiority has always been detested, and most thoroughly when greatest. A little care will serve to cloak your ordinary virtues, as you would hide your beauty, in careless dress.

Baltasar Gracian

A frown creasing my forehead, I read through the text again.

"Don't take it literally," Katan said, almost apologetically, perhaps sensing my confusion, or annoyance, or both. "That's what I want to talk to you about."

I dragged my glance away from the paper and met his brown eyes. "I'm all ears."

My former boss hesitated a moment, but when he spoke his tone was firm. "Rudy, you may be surprised to learn that a lot of people you encounter in your career may not react as favourably to you as you would like them to."

I frowned.

"Because of the person that you are, you're likely to face a lot of resentment, and even envy."

My frown intensified.

"People . . . insecure people, may very well see you as a threat." Katan paused, eyeing me, as if waiting for his words to sink in.

I nodded thoughtfully, but still unsure where he was headed with this. I resisted the temptation to glance at my watch. I'd never found comfort being the topic of discussion I'm involved in, or when others choose to dispense free advice. I much prefer to look deep within myself, or to books, for advice on how to live my life or manage my career.

Katan was shaking his head, slowly, ruefully. "Young man, I have learned over the years that people can be funny creatures, and I want you to listen very carefully to what I have to say."

I cleared my throat, and sat up in my seat.

"Managing relationships is a far more complex balancing act than balancing a ledger," he continued, fixing me with a firm stare. "In the real world, it's not just skill and ability that will see you through . . . it takes much more than that. The reality is that the better you perform in your job, the more people will resent you. And that resentment could come in many different ways."

He took a breather, then added, "And believe it or not, I can practically guarantee that you'll encounter a lot of people along the way who'll be gunning for you."

He sipped his coffee, spying me over the rim of his yellow mug.

I thought a moment then said, "I think I'm

beginning to understand what you mean. This world is full of insecure people. But that's not my fault. Neither is it my problem. I can't spend my time worrying about other people's insecurities. When I'm being paid to do a job, all that matters to me is that I do it to the best of my ability. That's my bottom line."

I realized I was getting worked up, so I took in a deep, quiet breath and tried to calm myself.

"Understood," said Katan with the tone of an adult trying to get through to a difficult child. "But remember that it is not just people at your level or even below you who may be insecure and cause trouble for you."

He paused, then spoke slowly. "It could very well be your boss himself."

My eyes narrowed to slits of cynicism. "My boss?"

"Yes, Rudy . . . your boss. And believe me, no one can pull the rug from under you faster than your boss . . . particularly if he sees you as a threat."

Katan paused, his gaze boring into me.

"But surely," I said, "This just doesn't seem logical. When I deliver the goods, my boss looks good. It's a symbiotic relationship, isn't it?"

"Not necessarily . . . I mean . . . yes . . . to some extent."

Katan took a deep breath before continuing. "The fact is, if you have a boss who is insecure about his own job or about himself, he may actually see you

260

as a threat and without you knowing it, your performance could actually undermine him."

I peered at the man as if he'd taken leave of his senses. "But don't all managers want their workers to work hard and to succeed. It's all about helping your department and the company achieve their objectives, isn't it?"

Katan was shaking his head, stubbornly. "Rudy, I know you find this difficult to relate to, but *trust* me on this one. I *know* what I'm saying." He lingered on the words 'trust' and 'know'.

"Okay . . . I hear you . . . so, how would you suggest I deal with this?"

A mischievous smile crossed his sagging face. "Have a look at the last sentence of the sheet of paper I gave you."

Picking up the slip, I whispered the words to myself:

A little care will serve to cloak your ordinary virtues, as you would hide your beauty, in careless dress.

Katan's voice cut through my thoughts. "It's clear, isn't it?"

Without moving my head, my eyes shifted to Katan's face. He was still smiling. I was still trying to assimilate the words. I wasn't getting it.

Then over the next few minutes my former boss lectured me on how *never* to outshine the master . . . the boss. It's all very simple, he said. To further one's career, one should play down one's strengths, particularly in the presence of insecure superiors. The boss should always be left feeling superior to you: flatter him; heap praise upon him; seek his advice even when you don't need it; make your brilliant ideas seem like his; even make the odd harmless mistake to make yourself seem as ordinary as he would want you to be.

"Abide by these rules," Katan advised, "and you will find that your boss may very well be happy to push your career along. And that's because you will seem less of a threat to him."

"But failing to abide by these rules," he countered, "could cause your boss to turn on you, and before you know the rug is pulled from under you, and you find yourself whittled out of his way, replaced by someone less competent, less effective, less threatening . . . leaving those around you to wonder what the hell's going on."

By the time Katan finished his dissertation, I felt dumb and stupid, and incredulous that I hadn't myself managed to interpret Gracian's words, that now seemed crystal clear. But I was equally incredulous that my former boss harboured such wisdom, considering the precarious state of his own career.

Doubt must have been plastered all over my face, for suddenly, firmly, Katan said, "Listen Rudy, my studies haven't been restricted to accounting books, you know. I have studied the works of great philosophers – you know – philosophers like Confucius, Machiavelli, Castiglione, Zagorin, Plutarch, Kautilya, Honoré de Balzac, Voltaire."

He paused, gazing at me the way that, I imagined, a father would gaze at a son. "These are tried and proven techniques. History is replete with the practical application of those strategies, and it may do you well in your spare time to study the works of great minds like Voltaire."

After a sip of cold coffee, Katan continued, his tone sombre, "Rudy, you don't know anything about me. But this job I'm doing now is nothing compared to previous positions I have held. You may not know it, but I have actually worked for two blue chip companies in the City, very high up in the finance department."

I kept nodding slowly, my brows arched slightly in surprise, as Katan continued, his eyes riveted on me.

"For years I survived and thrived because of these strategies which I'm trying to impart to you here today. The only reason I find myself in this position I'm in now is because I reached a stage in life where I just refused to play these games anymore. And as soon as I stopped, my world caved in on me . . . I became the victim of corporate politics."

Katan let out a series of lung-shaking coughs. When he continued, his tone was bitter and hoarse. "This is how I find myself working for this *stupid* little company in Milton Keynes, working for this *silly* little man who thinks he knows it all."

He coughed again. "So it is up to you to take my advice or not."

When, half an hour later, after Katan had regained his composure, I walked him out my office and down to reception, I'd already begun to see the man in a positively different light. It wouldn't be the first or the last time I'd misjudged a person.

"Thank you for all your advice," I said to him, injecting as much feeling as I could into the words and the expression on my face.

Katan smiled and tapped my shoulder, pleased he'd dispensed his dose of advice for the day.

The last thing I did before leaving my office at ten that evening, was to summarise, in my little black book, my friend's advice.

As my pen sped across the paper, I had no way of knowing then just how relevant this bit of advice would prove during a particularly challenging period in my career that was to come fifteen years later.

CHAPTER 22

I'd long ago learned not to shy away from making decisions – quick, effective decisions. As for the navigator, decisions steer the course, circumventing obstacles that litter the path to hoped-for prosperity. One's position in life reflects the decisions you've made along the way, much as the decisions you make today will determine your future. Of that I was certain.

Recently, I'd made some decisions. Tough decisions. I'd decided to give it all up. Everything. I needed to steer myself back on course.

When I found myself having to defer writing my finals because of unrelenting, uncompromising, work deadlines, I knew that something had to give. But it was more than that. It was also about what I was becoming. I was becoming too settled in this life of mine in the UK. I had the job, and the car, and recently I'd bought a house. This was crazy. I hadn't come here to stay; I was only meant to be passing through. I couldn't behave as

Rodney apparently had, and abandon the cause back home.

With that resolve, I gave it all up. The car, the house, the job. And I moved away from Milton Keynes. I moved northwards to Nottingham where, for three months, I would focus exclusively on getting my finals out of the way. I moved into the YMCA hostel, a two-minute walk from the Trent Polytechnic library where I planned to hit the books day and night, write my finals, and then fly back home, finally.

I'd decided.

That was three months ago.

Now, with soaring spirits, I stood on the cool pavement outside the examination hall. Eyes half-shut, I tilted my face towards the overcast November sky and took a long, deep breath of cool, fresh air into my lungs, and with a long, audible sigh of relief, expelled it. It felt like my first real breath in days.

Yes. I had done it. It was all over. Finally. Thank God.

Euphoria consumed every fibre of my being. With my finals at last over and done with, the very thought that I might soon again see my island, my home, my family, my friends, rippled a shiver of delight down my spine.

Moments later, briefcase in hand, I was sauntering nonchalantly down South Sherwood Street, in Robin Hood City, feeling on top of the world. If I'd had a tail I would have wagged it like a happy little pup.

As the examination hall receded slowly into the distance, I recounted my last few days.

For two brutal days I'd sat at the metal-framed desk in the packed examination hall, my pen scratching furiously across the paper as I tackled question after question with only slightly more gusto than during my practice sessions over the last three months in my cubicle at the polytechnic library.

But it was the adrenalin that had kept me going.

'Always rest the night before exams,' the experts had warned – warnings my mind had chosen to ignore. As I'd lain in bed, late evenings preceding the crucial days, despite debilitating fatigue my mind simply refused to quit. It refused to quit trying to answer past exam questions that lingered on in my head from the day before. When finally, in the early hours of the morning, my mind succeeding in switching itself off, I would invariably awake in panic, only to be overcome by enormous relief that I hadn't in fact overslept and missed my exams.

For two straight nights I'd slept hardly a wink. It was only the adrenalin flooding my cerebral cortex that had kept my faculties suitably in check; that had sharpened my focus during the two most important days of my life.

Now, as I rounded the corner into Mount Street, just one thought buzzed my mind; something I hadn't done for quite a while.

When, five blissful minutes later, I strode into the Victoria Shopping Centre, I strutted straight towards the Tesco supermarket and only stopped when I reached the section labelled 'liquor and alcohol'. Not ten minutes later, my right fingers firmly gripping the plastic ring securing the Heineken six-pack, briefcase swinging in the other hand, I virtually jogged into the two-storey Art Deco YMCA building on Shakespeare Street.

Bounding up the tiled stairs two at a time, I all but ran into a young lady donned in a shiny black track suit on the top landing.

"Sorry!" I panted.

When my eyes fell upon the smiling face before me, my heart skipped a beat.

"That's okay," she said, her voice soft and gentle, her magnificent smile illuminating not just her face but the entire passageway.

I was totally unprepared for this encounter. More than once I'd rehearsed in my mind lines I'd use to help me introduce myself to the gorgeous olive-skinned, mixed-race girl who seemed forever in the company of a heavily muscled, shaven-headed, middle-aged white man.

For an instant I felt an unfamiliar collision of excitement, thrill and bashfulness as I straightened a non-existent tie and cleared my throat.

"Hi," I said, desperately trying to control my breathlessness.

She continued to flash that warm, melting smile. "Hiya."

After an awkward silence in which I searched my mind for that knockout line, finally I spoke.

"I've seen you around here . . . um . . . in the canteen."

"Me too . . . I mean . . . I've seen you too."

"What's a girl like you doing in a place like . . ."

I couldn't believe I'd said that! Like an old car, I slowed, then stalled. I stalled because of the fleeting bout of nausea I felt as I balked at the tired chat-up line I'd so often vowed never to use. I could have kicked myself. I felt my face growing warmer and warmer.

To my complete amazement and delight, she didn't burst out laughing in my face. The lovely young lady simply continued to illuminate the entire place with that smile.

Then, forcefully, I had to stop myself from asking her age. I warned myself to stop being foolish, but noted that this beautiful girl couldn't be more than eighteen or nineteen. I wanted desperately to say something funny and interesting. But my brain seemed to have jammed.

"So . . . what's your name?" I said finally.

"Gina."

I introduced myself, extending my hand. When she reached out and took it, I felt her soft warmth caressing my clammy hand, glowing through my body. I resisted the urge to close my eyes and savour the moment.

"So, what's your hurry?" she asked, that smile still dancing upon her luscious lips.

"Well I've just finished my final accountancy exams . . ." I couldn't hold back the grin that hadn't stopped teasing my lips; it let itself loose, ". . . and I was just rushing up to my room to start my celebration."

I raised the Heineken six-pack before her eyes.

Gina turned the full force of her dazzling smile on me, but that had nothing to do with the six green cans. "Wow . . . you're an accountant . . . I've never met one of you lot before."

My grin broadened, and I forgot what I was about to say.

She ran a hand through her gorgeous black hair, adjusting a few loose strands that had fallen over her face.

After a brief, awkward silence, holding my breath, I heard myself say, "So, would you like to join me, in . . . umm . . . in celebrating my success?"

She hesitated a moment, then said, "I . . . I would like to but I'm on my way to . . ."

She paused, checked the large digital watch on her slim wrist and, to my utter delight, said, "How about a bit later?"

Slowly, I exhaled, feeling my pulse leaping.

"Sure," I said, staring at her long, curly, jet-black hair – hair that invoked a fleeting memory of Susanna.

"Say, seven thirty?"

"Sure."

"What's your room number?"

"Two zero seven."

She smiled. "Okay . . . see you then."

"Sure."

With a spring in my step, I strode down the long, dimly-lit corridor, bordered on both sides by guest bedrooms. I stood before room number 207. Fumbling the key into the door-lock, I pushed open the door, closed it slowly, leaned back against it and, giving the air a series of vicious upper-cuts, shouted, "Yes! *Yes*!! *Yes*!!!"

I was still grinning and panting when my eyes began to scan the little room. Thick books, lever-arch files, Kit Kat wrappers, Lucozade bottles littered the tiled floor. Piles of clothes carelessly draped the back of the folding metal chair that seemed on the verge of tilting over from the sheer weight. On the small wooden table next to the single bed that all but filled the entire room, a yellow mug grew its own life form, a puffy, greyish-green fungus that rose out of the mug. I hadn't had the time to wash that mug for well over a week . . . maybe two.

I glanced at my watch. With my special guest expected in just over two hours, I needed to clean up the mess – but only after I took care of some unfinished business. And that too, promised sheer pleasure.

I pulled a beer free from the pack, and leaped into the air, landing on my rump on the bed, ignoring its squeaky protest.

I cracked open my beer and brought the can up to my mouth, swallowing long and hard, smacking my lips in satisfaction. Then for a long, precious moment I closed my eyes and leaned back against the wall, feeling its coolness against the back of my head as I savoured the taste of my new-found freedom, and the attainment of my lifelong goal.

Taking another gulp of beer, I leaned forward, reaching out to the bottom of the bed for my brief-case. I clicked it open and extracted the thin blue booklet, the question paper from my last exam. Gone were the days when accountancy students were not allowed to remove question papers from the exam hall.

I felt a surge of adrenalin as I began to play the role of exam-marker, awarding myself marks for each question I'd attempted, then tallying my overall score.

Minutes later, realising I held an empty can in my hand, I flung the can towards the floor. It landed on the clothes-covered chair with a soft thud. I snatched another beer from the pack, pulled it open, set the can down on the bed between my thighs, then flipped to the first page of the question booklet.

Yesterday's review had gone well. I'd awarded myself an A and a B.

Now, meticulously going over the questions on this morning's paper, I reminded myself to remain objective, completely objective.

"You can't fool yourself, boy" I whispered.

For good measure, I decided to award the questions a 'pessimistic', 'optimistic', and 'most likely' score.

When fifteen blissful minutes later, my right index finger bounced off the minute keypad of my

Casio scientific calculator, the display revealed a most likely score of sixty-four, the average of the pessimistic and optimistic scores earlier computed.

I smiled, nursing my beer. I had a nice buzz going and was drinking at just the right pace to keep it that way.

I smiled more broadly, as a shiver rippled through me, made all the more profound when I recalled the treat that awaited me later this evening at seven thirty sharp.

Finding yet again that the can in my hand had got mysteriously light, I shook it and immediately cast it to the floor hearing the hollow, tinny sound reverberate through the room as it bounced off the vinyl tiles and rolled beneath the bed. Reaching for another, I reminded myself to save at least two for later.

This afternoon's paper in hand, my favourite subject – financial management – I tallied a pessimistic score of eighty-eight and succumbed to the grin that spread itself across my face. No need to go farther.

"A clear, outright Distinction," I whispered, feeling light-headed.

I clenched both my fists in front of me. "Yes! Thank You, God!" I shouted, as my eyes strayed across the narrow room to the sheet of paper taped to the front wall just above the little rectangular mirror. The scribbled words flowed from my lips like a nursery rhyme:

*The heights that great men reached and kept
were not attained by sudden flight,
But they, whilst their companions slept, were
toiling onwards through the night.*

For an instant, I was ten years old again, listening
to my primary-school headmaster at morning
assembly, as he urged students to memorise the
Thought for the week neatly chalked at the top left-
hand corner of the long blackboard set into the
wall.

"Let these words of wisdom be your companion
for life," the bespectacled Mr. Combie had implored.
To that end, I'd inscribed the words on the inside
cover of my every textbook; stuck it on every wall,
of every room I'd ever rented.

Returning my attention to the thin blue booklet
in my hand, I heaved yet another huge sigh before
shoving the paper back into my briefcase.

Yes. At long last, exams were behind me . . . a
thing of the past. The long journey had ended. I
had passed. All I needed now was formal confirmation, confirmation that would come in about
five weeks, confirmation of my actual results.

Feeling the warm glow of euphoria spreading
through me like blood through veins, I took another
sip from my beer, a roguish smile crossing my face.

"Tonight will make it even better," I whispered,
feeling a familiar stirring within me.

I took another pull from the can, deciding to tally
my scores again, for repeated pleasure.

I reached out to my opened briefcase at the bottom of the bed, and retrieved the question paper. But I noted it felt a bit thicker this time.

I twisted over the bounded sheets, and . . .

I froze. Then I felt a swooping sensation and a violent jolt in my heart, as if I'd just fallen through a hole in a board floor.

Struck dumb, I blinked, my eyebrows arched in horrified bewilderment. I swallowed hard and blinked again, feeling the blood rushing to my head, feeling the bed tilting beneath me, feeling dazed.

In stunned disbelief my bulging eyes blazed at the horror before me.

"What the . . . ?!"

CHAPTER 23

I felt as though a thousand volts had just zapped right through me. Heart thumping, panic-stricken eyes transfixed to the thin white booklet in my hand, desperately I willed the wretched thing to disappear.

It didn't.

A deep, demented frown creasing my forehead, my eyes shot down to the can on the bed between my thighs, wondering whether the two Heinekens I'd just thrown down were messing with my mind.

Not sure.

Breathing in short, shallow gasps, my eyes jerked back to the booklet now weighing a ton in my hand.

I clenched my eyes shut, shaking my head vigorously. When, several seconds later my eyes shot open, the wretched thing defiantly stood its ground, staring boldly up at me.

For a fleeting instant I just sat there, convinced this was not really happening to me, this was a dream, I thought wildly, or else I had gone mad.

I pinched my arm, hoping to awake in my bed. Nothing. I must have gone mad.

Horrified, stiffly I rose to my feet.

I stood there besides the bed, shaking, clutching the white booklet, feeling a groundswell of tension ebbing through my body, a giddy wave of nausea shuddering through my core.

A loud intense whisper that had begun in the pit of my stomach, ripped out from my throat. "No! No! *No!*"

My hand jerked the bound sheets of paper up to my blazing eyes. On the front page, I saw scribbles – scribbles that I instantly recognized, my own scribbles: on the top right-hand corner, my name; beneath that, my student registration number, next, the words *Financial Management*.

"God! No! No! No!"

I flipped over the page, and instantly felt my body sway from the sudden wave of giddiness that again swept through me. I began to see twinkling stars against a stark blackness. I reached out, steadying myself against the left lateral wall.

As the darkness slowly receded, and as my eyes re-focused on the page in front of me, again I saw my scribble blinking at me: my name, my registration number, then the subject – *Financial management.*

I felt my blood pressure surge when I recognised the answer I'd scratched out to question number one on the Efficient Market Hypothesis.

"Oh no! *No!! No!!!*" I shouted, the words

reverberating bitterly through my head, echoing through the room.

No longer in doubt, the realisation chilled me to the bone. Dumbfounded, I stood in the middle of the room, still swaying in the fog of head rush, my mind a swirl of confusion, tasting despair like salt in my mouth.

"How the hell could this happen?" Over and over again I kept repeating the words, as a thousand other questions jostled about in my head.

"How the hell could my answer booklet have found its way into my briefcase? How? How? *How?*"

I paused. My jaw dropped. My hand shot up clasping my gaping mouth, my bulging eyes threatening to pop out their sockets.

For an instant, my mind fled back to the examination hall.

"Pens down please!" the lead invigilator had repeated, her stern voice resounding in the large hall. I crossed my last 't', then cast the blue PaperMate down on the desk, adding to the cacophony of five hundred pens hitting desks' wooden surfaces. I'd smiled in satisfaction and relief, as I craned my neck to scan the sea of faces all around me, trying to read expressions.

"Papers, please," said the elderly gentleman, the assistant invigilator, shuffling down the aisle.

A quick glance at my desk confirmed that all was fine – my answer booklet lay next to a set of bound, unused graph paper. Good.

Closing my eyes, I'd leaned back in my seat savouring the satisfaction of what I considered my best paper to date, knowing it was my last.

I heard the lethargic, grey-haired, bespectacled, elderly gentleman advance to my desk. "Papers, please."

I heard his nails scratch against the desk-top as he scraped up my answer booklet before moving on to the candidate in front of me.

This man must be at least a hundred years old, I remembered thinking.

When the five hundred-odd finalists were dismissed, the enormous hall erupted in a rumble of voices amid the sound of metal chairs grating on ceramic tiles. Rising to my feet, I wished the apprehensive-looking Asian man to my left the very best of luck. We shook hands as he returned the sentiment. Feeling instantly light-headed, I'd absently picked up off the desk my pen, calculator, ruler, question paper and graph paper, and shoved them into my briefcase.

The hollow, tinny, sound of a can hitting the bare vinyl tile yanked me back to the present.

My suspicion hit me with the force of a speeding truck. In a frenzied rush, I spilled the contents of my briefcase out over the bed. Searching frantically, my eyes found no graph paper – not a sheet.

I felt a knot tightening in my stomach. The words I was about to utter echoed bitterly in my head before spewing from my mouth.

"The senile old fool picked up the unused graph sheets instead of my bloody answer booklet! What I picked up off the desk and placed in my brief-case was my answer booklet . . . not the unused graph paper. God! I'm in trouble!"

The graph paper, I recalled in horror, mirrored the answer booklet – same colour and same space to insert name, registration number, and subject.

Realizing the daunting implications of my horrific plight, I felt emotions I'd never felt before surging through my subconscious, crushing, stabbing at me. And during the ensuing few seconds, a dozen conflicting thoughts whirled through the chaotic turbulence of my mind, the foremost being the need for urgent haste.

Moments later I was bounding down the long flight of steps leading to the exit, hoping and praying I might reach the examination hall before the invigilators left without my script.

I exploded onto the courtyard, gasping for breath, clutching the booklet. Every muscle in my body was tuned to just this one objective. A journey that had taken twenty long minutes this morning, now took no more than five, though it felt like an hour.

One way or the other, time was evaporating rapidly.

As the enormous building came into view, I dashed across the courtyard, hoping and praying. The building seemed to grow bigger and bigger as

I sprinted towards it, my eyes frantically scanning the entrance.

As I reeled to a stop before the massive structure, all hope died; my heart sank. Panting, I stared dumbfounded at the two heavy oak front doors that were solidly shut.

Damn! I grabbed the long brass handles and shook them violently. Nothing. I banged and banged. Nothing. I peered through the keyhole. Nothing.

The huge hall, just minutes ago bustling with activity, now seemed empty, deserted, silent.

I spun on my heels, my eyes darting frantically across the car park for any sign of activity. Nothing.

The invigilators had disappeared . . . they had come to do a job . . . they had done it . . . they had collected the examination scripts . . . all but one. Mine. And they had vanished.

As the concrete structure loomed before me, drawing a shuddering breath, eyes tight shut, I put my hot head, dripping with sweat, in my hands, and leaned forward against the oak doors, feeling their coarse texture against the back of my hands, my nostrils taking in the earthy scent of the weather-beaten wood.

My mind raced. I felt disaster. A deep gloom had already spread through me like a wave of acid. As I stood there in a swirl of confusion and dismay, I weighed my options. *What options?* My mind was a mass of muddled thoughts. Then, in my plight I suddenly felt a door inside me open, revealing, somewhere in the distance, a dim ray of hope.

I bolted off again, my feet pounding the concrete pavement. Bemused eyes followed me as I scurried past them. Mothers pulled infants out of harm's way. A little old lady pushing a trolley stiffened and adjusted her purse strap as she caught sight of me approaching. I swerved past her trolley, all but running into a throng of young men gathered on the pavement, their angry voices following me as I bolted blindly down the road.

Paying no heed to the screeching of rubber tyres on the asphalt road, or to the angry, cursing voices, or to the protesting car horns, my mind was a chaotic turbulence.

When I reeled around the corner, I caught sight of the narrow brick building, my last hope. I broke into spontaneous prayer. *Please God . . . Please!* This was my one last chance; I needed all the help I could get. Now, more than ever, I needed divine intervention.

Picking up my pace, I only stopped running when I crashed against the counter, startling the dark-haired, middle-aged uniformed officer who sat at the small desk behind the small cubicle.

"Please," I gasped, my expression wrought with panic. "I need your help."

The officer eyed me, his taut face devoid of expression.

"How can we help you sir?" His tone was formal . . . businesslike.

I was still panting. "My exam . . . I've just written my final accounting exam and . . . and I don't know how, but . . . but I managed to walk out of the exam room with the script in . . . in my . . . in my briefcase."

Like a judge pondering my fate, the officer frowned, studying my face with unmistakeable suspicion.

I was breathing deeply now. "I really don't know how it happened, but I would like the police to hold my script for me until Monday morning and to post it to the examining body."

I held out the answer booklet.

He didn't believe me. I could read it in his eyes. The officer's frown intensified. "I'm sorry, sir?" he said, his tone incredulous.

I swallowed hard. "I took home my exam answer booklet by mistake, I went to look for the invigilators but they had already left. I would really appreciate it if you could hold on to it for safekeeping over the weekend so that I can call the examination board. They need to know that the paper was in safe hands and that I haven't tampered with it."

I could see naked scepticism on his face, his eyes narrowed to slits of suspicion. "You want me to hold on to your test?"

"Yes," I nodded, breathing heavily. "Please. I'm really desperate . . . I really need your help. I'm in a lot of trouble here."

I pushed the booklet across the counter, but, the officer boomeranged it right back. "I'm sorry sir, but we can't do that."

The pale-faced man sternly turned his back,

seemingly uninterested in winning any customer service awards.

"Please mate . . . I assure you I did not tamper with the paper. I went home and just found the thing in my briefcase."

He turned once more to face me, his voice steely. "Sir, this is not a matter for the police."

"Come on, man!" I said, a bit more forcefully than intended.

He glared at me. "Sir, we are not a charity. I suggest that you get a priest to hold it for you, or arrange to take your test again."

I hated that patronising tone.

Blankly, I stared at the hatch that had just shut in my face.

I felt as if the entire ground had caved in and I was tumbling down the bottomless pit of despair.

I bit my lip, but still I did not awaken from the nightmare.

My voice was lifeless with humiliation when I spoke again. "Please officer . . . please."

But the voice emanating from behind the hatch was clipped, final. "Please move away from the counter, sir."

For what seemed an eternity, I stared listlessly at the white, vinyl hatch covering, feeling that now-familiar knot tightening in my stomach, that awful, sickening feeling. My mind hazed with fatigue, confusion, despair.

I turned and leaned back against the warm concrete façade of the police station, and very slowly slid my body down to the ground. I felt the coarseness of the wall grating my back.

Seated on the cool pavement, feet pulled up under my thighs, I leaned forward and rested my head over my crossed arms, the creased, sweat-dampened booklet dangling from my hand.

A succession of incoherent thoughts flashed through my mind, each cast out as quickly as it entered.

Then I heard the officer's words resonating dismally in my mind – *"We are not a charity . . . get a priest . . . get a priest . . . a priest . . . a priest . . ."*

I was scratching my head, lost.

Out of the blue, something . . . something of life-saving importance . . . occurred to me.

My head shot up.

"A priest!" I shouted.

Springing to my feet, I was off again, like a madman bolting down the street.

It took me all of five minutes to reach the YMCA building, and all of five seconds to bolt up the stairs to the first floor.

"Please come in," the soft, gentle voice said in response to the loud, aggressive banging on his office door.

My thoughts were a blur as I pushed open the door into the cramped office that was laced with the scent of burning incense. From behind thick-rimmed spectacles and a copy of the Holy Bible, a bald, late-middle-aged man with auburn hair and a friendly face glanced up at me.

I was still panting as the back of my hand wiped away the sweat running down my forehead, and into my eyes, stinging.

"Rudy?" The man dressed in black, with a white collar, seemed startled by my apparent shell-shocked appearance. With some exertion, he hoisted himself up from his seat and strode towards me.

I swallowed hard against the lump in my throat. "Father Hunte, I really, really need your help."

"Of course, lad. Sit down; tell me what's happened." It'd been a while since I'd seen an expression as kind as the one etched on the man's lined face as he stood looking up at me.

I accepted a seat on the upholstered chair next to the window. In weak, faltering tones I explained my predicament, occasionally shifting my gaze out onto the desolate-looking series of grey rooftops huddled closely together.

From behind his desk, the resident manager of the Nottingham YMCA looked politely incredulous as he listened. Then, shaking his balding head in apparent sympathy, he said, in his soft, cultured voice, "And how do you suppose I can help you, lad?"

His eyes now communicated his sorrow, his understanding, his willingness to assist in whatever way he could. I felt a tinge of hope.

"Can you please keep this in a safe place for me over the week-end . . . until Monday?"

I handed him the creased, damp booklet, its pages folded down at the corners. It looked nowhere near as important as it was to me.

The priest took the booklet, straightening out the dog-ears with his palms. Gingerly, he set the bounded sheets on the desk before him, sat still and quiet, apparently in deep introspection, eyeing the document.

I was still holding my breath when the bells of a nearby belfry rang out, resonating through the little room like suspense from a horror movie.

Father Hunte slowly glanced up at me, sympathy in his hazel eyes. "Sure . . . I can keep it safely for you over the weekend."

I exhaled long and hard, my heart leaping in sudden relief.

"Thank you, Father . . . thank you very, very much. I really do appreciate your help."

I felt the tension that had besieged me begin to ebb away. Emboldened, I felt an idea popping into my mind.

Breathless, I uttered the words quickly, feeling my heart fluttering. "Father, would you mind writing a letter to the accountancy body, explaining to them what transpired?"

"Of course lad . . . of course."

My heart was now leaping in joy. I felt an instantaneous and unexpected surge of hope.

The ancient typewriter that he pulled across the desk squeaked against the wood surface. Inserting a letter-sized sheet of paper, the kindly priest glanced up at me expectantly. Fingers poised over the keys he asked, "What would you like me to say?"

I thought quickly – *the board must know that I did not deliberately remove the paper from the hall; their sympathy should be invoked; they must believe I hadn't tampered with the paper; they must give me the benefit of the doubt . . .*

I dictated, as if to my secretary. Like a skilled secretary, the priest typed away.

The clicking sound of the typewriter had a strangely calming effect on me, made all the more profound by the sight of a man of God depressing the keys, *sending a message from God*. I found myself wondering about the religious affiliation of those who would decide my fate, hoping that politics and religion would conspire to find favour for me. I needed all the help I could get.

His eyes riveted on the paper before him, his forehead creased in concentration, the priest read out each sentence before pulling the carriage-return lever across. On official YMCA letterhead, he explained my plight, asking for compassion, vouching for my character.

"Now all we can do is hope and pray." He smiled sympathetically.

He signed the letter, then folded it neatly into the envelope on which he'd typed the London address I'd given him and, along with that all-important booklet, locked it away into a small steel safe set in the wall, behind a portrait of a distinguished-looking clergyman. "You have worked extremely hard, and it's out of your hands now. It's in the Lord's hand."

"Thank you, Father, thank you." Rising to my feet, I pumped the priest's warm hand. I found myself, rather oddly, thinking – *here is a man destined for heaven*.

He smiled modestly, seemingly in the knowledge that he was doing God's work.

"Try and rest – you look exhausted."

With enormous relief, I nodded and made my way out of the small office. Eyeing the sterile, white tiles as I tottered down the corridor, my legs still shaky, towards my room, I hoped and prayed – hoped for the best, and prayed that my lingering fear wouldn't materialise.

When I entered the familiar surroundings of the tiny room, all I could do was collapse on the narrow bed, on top of the scattered contents of my briefcase.

Lost in slumber, seven thirty came and went. I never heard the gentle knocking on the door.

CHAPTER 24

Nightmares tormented my sleep. I rolled over onto my left side, trying to escape from a dream where a shuffling wrinkled creature chased me down a dark alley as I struggled to run as fast as I could, but in slow motion.

When I awoke with a start, it took several moments before it all came flooding back.

A deep gloom overwhelmed me. I shook my pounding head, trying to blot out the images marching across my mind: the stern face of the unyielding police officer; that old, wrinkled, shuffling invigilator; images of me running through the streets of Nottingham like a madman.

I hoisted myself up from the bed, the movement requiring the full strength of both arms, my body shuddering from the dizzying exertion. I felt a prickly sensation shivering through my skin, alternating hot and cold. And I felt lifeless, devoid of energy, completely spent, heartbroken several times over.

Despite Father Hunte's God-given gesture, I now floundered in a sea of pessimism.

The sight of my books splayed over the floor only served to deepen my gloom.

Groggily, I glanced down at my watch. It had just gone half past one in the afternoon. My watch also told me that today was Sunday. *Sunday?* My mind hazed in confusion. Then it dawned. I had slept through Saturday and half of Sunday. But even so, my eyelids felt as though they were weighed down with lead.

Though I felt acid eating away at the walls of my stomach – a nauseous, burning sensation – I had no desire for food. But I knew I needed to eat something. I made the daunting journey down to the canteen on the floor below, and bought a portion of fish and chips which I brought up to my room. I stared at the plate a long while before dumping its contents in the bin besides my little table.

I was totally spent, my mind and body drained of vital nutrients . . . nutrients I needed to survive . . . if I wanted to.

I collapsed again across the bed, and closed my eyes, oblivious to everything but the torment searing my mind.

I slept. I dreamed. I awoke on Monday to the same dark gloom. After a quick shower, I stepped out of my room with crippling self-consciousness, and made my way stiffly across the corridor and down the stairs to the office on the first floor. When Father Hunte handed me the registered postal slip for the letter he'd mailed, I felt optimism returning – a dim, distant ray of hope. But I couldn't shake off the fatigue that overwhelmed every fibre of my being.

Over the next few days, my heart hammering with fear and hope, I kept to my room, feasting on bottles of Lucozade and packets of Kit Kat, ignoring the gentle knocking on my door. Company . . . I didn't need.

When on Thursday morning I was awakened by a shuffling sound, something being forced under my door, I froze, realizing what it might be. Despite the sleep in my eyes, my mind snapped to attention, and for a fleeting moment my spirit leaped with sudden hope . . . hope that instantly evaporated.

For a long uncertain moment, teetering on the brink of panic, I stared at the thin, white envelope on the tiled floor in front of the door. I realized I wasn't breathing; I exhaled the spent air. Then, like a weary animal, instinctively distrusting a potentially lethal foe, apprehensively I moved in closer to the envelope.

My heart was fluttering wildly as I reached down a shaky, sweaty hand and picked up the envelope. Tearing off one side, I pulled out the folded sheet of paper.

My heart skipped a beat. It was *the* letter. My heart was thumping away. I read.

Dear Mr Gurley,

I appreciate that you must have been very distressed by the situation resulting from your taking away your examination script from the examination hall at Nottingham.

There has never been an instance where the Examination Committee has felt it possible to allow a script, once removed from the hall, to be marked. I will, however, bring your situation and the circumstances to the Committee's attention.

I am very sorry that this has happened, and very much hope that you will be successful next time you sit.

Director – EXAMINATIONS

By the time I'd read through the last line, the room had already begun to spin. I steadied myself against the table and took a seat on the edge of the bed. I shut my eyes. When I opened them, the stubborn room was still in a swirl, this time in slow motion. Then, reluctantly, it came to a halt.

Swallowing hard against the painful knot of misery congealing in my throat, I read again. And again. Each time I felt my world slipping farther and farther away.

I heard the sound of bells, vague and distant as they rang out from the belfry, images of the kindly priest flashing before me.

I read through the second-last line: *I will, however,*

bring your situation and the circumstances to the Committee's attention.

The words echoed in my head. Like a drowning man clutching at straws, I held on to the words. A tiny spurt of hope burgeoned in my chest, but was immediately strangled by panic when I read the last paragraph: *I am very sorry that this has happened, and very much hope that you will be successful next time you sit.*

Now I felt myself sinking, sinking down the murky depths of despair.

My mind groped for different interpretations of the words, as varying degrees of optimism and pessimism swept through me, hot and cold. A part of me told me there was hope yet; *hold on, don't give up.* Another, more forceful, part urged me to accept the reality; the words were eloquently clear. *So, accept it and move on.* I felt myself succumbing to the more powerful voice. The message was clear to me. A subtle rejection. I had failed. I'd have to retake all four papers. All four. The very thing I'd feared had come to pass.

Preparing to rewrite these subjects would be like pushing that boulder up that steep hill all over again, my mind told me.

I felt my dreams, my aspirations, come crashing down like a gigantic wave splashing and foaming away into oblivion.

The room settled into silence around me. Occasionally I heard footsteps outside my door, bouncing off the sterile vinyl tiles, an echoing, clicking sound.

In the little rectangular mirror on the wall across the little room, I caught a reflection of myself.

A pathetic, thin, washed-out face glared back at me. I hardly recognised the stranger with that dark stubble shrouding his jaw and chin. This wasn't the face of the young man who, only three months before, had sat in an executive office managing a twenty-strong finance department. These weren't the eyes of the man who, last Friday, had strolled down South Sherwood Street nonchalantly, convinced that he had seen an examination hall for the last time ever. This was the troubled face of a man, dishevelled, tormented; a man who had apparently seen more than his fair share of misery.

Rousing myself, my gaze shifted to my shaking hands and to the letter that they clutched. I breathed in deeply, my lungs filling with the stale, stuffy air that hovered around my cluttered room. My mind hazed, and when I exhaled slowly, I felt no better.

"God . . . what did I do to deserve this?" I said in a wan, hoarse voice that I barely recognized as my own.

Over the next few days, I spent virtually all my time shut away indoors. I slept, and slept, hardly eating. When finally, on the third day of misery, I ventured down to the television room on the first floor, for a moment I was convinced I'd found myself in a lunatic asylum.

A short Chinese man, in his mid-thirties, who I'd earlier seen moving about sullenly in fluffy black bedroom slippers, sat quietly near the back of the medium-sized room. A lanky, pimple-faced skin-head with a swastika emblazoned on his forehead, clad in an old bomber jacket, jeans and knee-high steel-toed combat boots, sat alone at the back, looking angry with the world and with himself.

It wasn't two minutes after the skinhead had stormed out of the room, apparently disgusted about something, that the Chinese pulled his chair alongside mine.

"It's bad," he said in a strong Asian cadence, as we watched a replay of last year's Tiananmen Square disaster on BBC One.

Not at all keen on conversation, I nodded blankly.

"We're safe here, though," he continued, his slitted eyes darting frequently across to the side entrance, as though at any moment he expected trouble to walk in through the door.

"Are you okay?" I asked, hardly caring one way or the other.

He nodded nervously, and remained silent a long while. Then, like a private detective, he began firing questions at me: "Who are you? Where are you from? What are you doing here? Can you under-stand Mandarin Chinese?"

I responded in as few words I could find.

Then he fired another question. "You ever heard of the Triads?"

I thought a moment. Late last year I'd watched a TV documentary on the violent gangs involved in organised crime in Hong Kong – 'the Chinese Mafia', the narrator had called them.

"Sure," I said.

After a long, empty pause, the Oriental man again pulled my eyes off the screen.

"You see me . . . I look like a simple man living in this place, but you know nothing about me," he said, sounding as though someone had done him some great injustice.

I frowned, returning my attention to the television mounted up on a bracket hanging from the ceiling.

I don't need this. I have enough on my plate.

But the man continued speaking, as if to himself. "I have a wife and two lovely kids back home in Hong Kong."

I turned to face him. His head was bowed mournfully.

"They haven't seen me for three years. I had to disappear one night . . . they maybe think I'm dead."

My eyebrows furrowed with sudden interest. His eyes remained fixed to the floor.

"I used to be a very well-off solicitor back home in Hong Kong. I was a senior manager in a large law firm in Central, the financial district."

Sure that the man was lying through his teeth, I chose silence.

"In one night I lost everything . . . my wife, my children, my job, my money . . . everything." With the back of his hand, he wiped away the tears streaming down his yellow cheeks.

For a brief moment our eyes met, and I sensed his sorrow, his distress, his loneliness, his fear.

With growing interest, I then listened to a tale worthy of a Hollywood script. In a faltering voice, he described in horrific detail a Triad killing he'd witnessed. He'd been on the run since then. Without a word of goodbye to his family, he'd fled Hong Kong. The Triads had put a contract out on his head. Because of their power and international links, he feared he could never be safe.

Though the man seemed an excellent storyteller, I wasn't buying.

Out of sheer mischief, I decided to test the self-proclaimed solicitor's knowledge of business law.

His face lit up as he supplied, in formal legal language, answers to questions on cases I'd studied as part of my business law course. He went on to quote cases, dates, outcomes, legal principles, precedence. When he eloquently summarised *Solle v Butcher*, the well-known case decided upon by Lord Denning, I was astonished. At that instant, I became convinced the man was the real thing. I felt nothing but sympathy for the short, bespectacled, middle-aged Chinese man whose burdens seemed etched on his anguished face. I understood now, why he had seemed so reclusive.

But in no way was I prepared for what happened next.

Without the slightest warning, he bolted to his feet, his face congealed in horror.

"Who are you! Why are you after me!" he demanded, his voice raised, his eyes smouldering with fear and panic.

I blinked, confused, astonished.

"No, no . . . I'm not after you," I said, sounding as if I was trying to talk someone out of jumping off a high-rise building.

A moment later he was bolting out the room, shouting, "Leave me alone! Leave me alone!"

For a long, confused moment, I stood frowning at the opened doorway. My astonishment intensified further when a dark-skinned man of medium height and build, wearing a black leather jacket over jeans, strode into the room.

Up until then I'd assumed I was the only black male at the Nottingham YMCA. In some strange way, it was a comforting development.

"What's with Chong?" he asked, looking puzzled as he pulled up a chair and sat a few seats to my left, apparently keen on catching the latest football results. "The guy almost sent me flying." The Jamaican accent was undeniable.

I shrugged, feigning ignorance.

Our eyes shifted to the large television screen. My mind replayed the events of the last half hour, somewhat troubled about the state of mind of the poor Chinese fellow.

After catching the football scores, we introduced ourselves.

"So why are you here?" he probed, like one prison inmate to another.

I thought a moment before answering. "I've been hibernating here over the last few months preparing for some exams . . . and you?"

As I listened to the Jamaican, I kept wondering whether April the First had come early. It seemed like a day for practical jokes, for I was taking on board yet another story worthy of the big screen.

The Jamaican, seemingly in his early thirties, claimed to have been engaged in a life of crime, serious crime, as a member of the infamous Jamaican gang, the Yardies.

First it was the peculiar Chinese talking about the Triads, now this Jamaican was talking about the Yardies.

"Some things," he sighed, "will haunt me for the rest of me life."

I searched the man's face for a hint of a joke. He looked dead serious. But he also looked nothing like a criminal. He lacked that vicious, hardened look that can so easily intimidate.

In a tremulous voice, he described how, six months ago, he'd reached his lowest ebb, troubled as he was by the never-ending cycle of violence he was caught up in. When one afternoon he found himself standing on the rooftop of a twelve-storey building in Birmingham, contemplating jumping off the edge to an untimely end, he had a seemingly miraculous, life-redeeming experience. The Jamaican claimed to have heard, from out of nowhere, a disembodied male voice urging him to seek the way of the Lord.

I said nothing, but the cynical expression crossing my face provoked a response from the man who seemed overcome by emotion.

"I swear on me mother's *life*." He stressed the last word. His voice intensified, his eyes glistening, he continued. "I heard the voice, man . . . it was real . . . as real as you're here, now, talking to me. As I speak about it now, shivers passing through me. Look at me skin, man . . . is pure truth me talking."

Pulling up his sleeve, he stretched out his arm, revealing dark skin covered in goose bumps.

Upon hearing the voice, he'd stepped away from the rooftop, and away from his life of crime. He believed he was divinely guided to the Seventh Day Adventist church in Nottingham. He was now pursuing a career in theology.

Though in the man's eyes I saw nothing but sincerity, my mind had great difficulty buying the story. But my heart didn't. My heart won hands down when I looked into his eyes and saw that it glistened with contentment such as I'd never seen in anyone. It was as though the mere mention of God, or Jesus, produced a heightened state of euphoria that shone through his eyes.

I spoke of my days at the SDA Academy in St. Lucia, and how I wouldn't have achieved a secondary education had it not been for that institution.

"This was your fate, man . . . divine intervention," the Jamaican said, as he rose to leave. This time, I had no reason to doubt these last words . . . he was speaking my kind of language.

When I got up and walked slowly back towards

the sanctuary of my room, my mind was buzzing with the incredible stories I'd heard this evening. For a while, my own predicament seemed pale in comparison to the alleged experiences of the two men; two men from completely different worlds, who, like books, had opened up their lives to me.

As I passed the games room along the narrow corridor I felt my heart lurch when I glimpsed Gina again, her lovely face accented by high cheekbones and exotic eyes, her long black hair pulled back into a sleek ponytail. My face flushed slightly when it dawned upon me that I'd completely forgotten our rendezvous, but equally I marvelled at how quickly the excitement I'd felt early that evening had diminished, replaced by more despondent preoccupations.

I wondered whether she had in fact showed up at my door.

I couldn't so much as muster the slightest of smiles as I approached her, recoiling as soon as I glimpsed, from the corners of my eyes, the muscular figure of the middle-aged, shaven-headed white man lining up a shot at the pool table. Gina shot me a warning glance. But something in her eyes hinted at displeasure, something that went beyond the mere presence of her muscled companion.

My face reddened as I wheeled and retraced my steps out of the room, only slightly perturbed that I'd apparently blown my chances.

As I stepped into my little room, I dropped to my knees and, reaching under the bed, pulled out a dusty haversack and retrieved from it an orange lever-arch file. For the first time in a week, I smiled as my eyes fell upon the large white sticker bearing the scribbled letters that spelt EMERGENCY KIT.

I'd almost forgotten its existence.

Sitting on the side of the bed, I ran my fingers along the edges of the file, recalling all those years ago in Lewisham when I'd built up my collection after my disastrous first accounting assignment.

I flipped through pages, reading the motivational poems and phrases aloud.

One line in particular leapt out at me: *Many men owe the grandeur of their lives to their tremendous difficulties.*

The words resonated in my mind as I recounted the events of the last few days, surprised that my face didn't congeal instantly into a painful grimace.

And I smiled when I read the passage that suggested that most people's greatest success comes just after their greatest failure.

Then I thumbed the photocopied magazine articles on the lives and accomplishments of great men. As I'd done four years earlier, I read the uplifting story of Fred Smith, the founder of FedEx – his domestic struggles, his business challenges, and his eventual phenomenal success. Then I read the story of Thomas Edison, with his incredible tenacity, his innumerable failures, and his historic success.

Finally, a few pages down, my eyes settled on one of my favourite poems. I whispered the words.

When things go wrong, as they sometimes will,
When the road you're trudging seems all uphill
When the funds are low and the debts are high
And you want to smile, but you have to sigh

When care is pressing you down a bit
Rest if you must, but don't you quit.
Life is queer, with its twists and turns,
As every one of us sometimes learns,
And many a failure turns about

When he might have won had he stuck it out.
Don't give up though the pace seems slow
You may succeed with another blow!

Success is failure turned inside out –
The silver tint of the clouds of doubt,
And you can never tell how close you are,
It may be near when it seems so far.

So stick to the fight when you're hardest hit –
It's when things seem worst that you must not quit.

As I often did, I wondered about the anonymous poet who'd penned those lines.

I began to feel my strength, my zeal for life, returning. I felt the deep gloom that had so overwhelmed me those last few days gradually begin to wane.

Over the next week, I sweated in the basement gym – pumping iron, stamping treadmills, riding exercise bikes. As I powered my way through the equipment, my mind dissected the events of the previous two weeks. Gradually, I came to accept the reasonableness and wisdom of the exam board's decision. I couldn't blame anyone for the fiasco but me. Even the decrepit invigilator I took off the hook. The resentful fire that had burned within me had been quelled.

Sitting in my room one evening after a vigorous workout, feeling a wave of inspiration washing over me, I reached for my little black book and scribbled down my thoughts:

> *My experience in Nottingham was an act of divine intervention; I see it now. This is good for me – this is a correction to bring me back on course. I will move to London, get a new and exciting job, broaden my experience, meet new people. In due course I will see the silver lining of the cloud that had threatened to derail me.*

It was time to move on.

CHAPTER 25

The London City YMCA, located on Errol Street in the heart of the City of London, was a five-minute walk from the Barbican Centre, Europe's largest multi-arts and conference venue. The five-storey, one-hundred-and-twelve-bed hostel and conference facility had been established in 1985. Although having similar goals to other YMCA hostels, the London City branch stood out because its service and décor mirrored an upscale hotel, and housed mainly young professionals.

This is where fate led me after my dam of grief had finally broken six weeks before. I'd had my eyes on the place ever since I'd visited a friend who stayed there back in 1987. The hostel, therefore, was my choice of residence on re-entry into London.

Banks of recessed spot lights in the suspended ceiling ensured that the well-appointed canteen, teeming with people, was brightly lit. Young men and women queued up for the delectable buffet laid out near the back of the hall. Others sat around tables, knives and forks in hand, digging into plate-fuls, chatting away animatedly. The buzz of voices, mingled with classical background music, sounded like a church congregation praying together.

It was around the rectangular table in the centre of the canteen that I sat with my companions. They were discussing, as they did daily, the delights of classical music, a topic that I found as inspiring as the sterile ceramic tiles covering the floor. All the while, my eyes roamed the room. Not for the first time, I found mine the only black face in sight, though I spotted one or two individuals seemingly of Asian descent.

James, a blue-eyed blond of average height and build, sounded distinctly aristocratic with his cut-glass English intonation. "From what I've read and heard, Bach is now considered somewhat atypical as far as Baroque composers go. His obsession with the fugue was apparently rather anachronistic. In fact, most other composers of the same era held that the fugue was an out-dated form."

"Obviously," Edward chipped in, sounding equally polished, "the man must have had an affinity for poetry because he set so much of it to music."

I was clearly out of my depth.

"Didn't he write the poem 'Edifying Thoughts of a Tobacco Smoker?" asked another bespectacled young man around our table.

James nodded, smiling enigmatically. He pushed out his chest, took a deep breath, and, in his erudite accent, blurted out theatrically, "On land, on sea, at home, abroad, I smoke my pipe and worship God."

Laughter rippled across the table. I chipped in with a mild chuckle, but my mind wandered.

As with every community, the London City YMCA had its cliques. Though I had little affinity with the aristocratic Englishmen, they were my clique. When, on my first visit to the canteen four weeks before, I'd stood, tray in hand, eyes searching for a vacant seat in the packed hall, James had courteously invited me to his table in the centre of the hall. Since then, like old chums, we were drawn to sitting together.

Like my companions, I was wearing a dark, single-breasted business suit with my tie loosened around my neck. Having only minutes before snaked my car through thick city traffic, at the end of a long day I was relieved to find a parking place in Errol Street, right in front of the hostel. My first company car, a red Ford Escort, would incur no parking fines in that location.

My latest accounting position, at a large vehicle-leasing firm, had, like my two previous permanent jobs, been the result of a temporary contract. Nancy, my agent, had been pleased to hear from me upon my return to London. She soon got me back onto the contract accounting scene. Three weeks later, my temporary assignment turned permanent when the finance director offered me the position of management accountant, along with a nineteen-thousand-pound annual salary and a red Ford Escort.

Nottingham was a thing of the past. I was well down the road to discovering the silver lining of that cloud that had hung so ominously over my head.

A particular event, however, had threatened to bring it all back. That was the day my exam results had arrived in the mail. My heart had been pounding hard and fast as I'd stood in the centre of my room, envelope in hand. When I'd opened the envelope and pulled out the results slip, the first word that greeted my wary eyes was FAIL. Though the result was hardly surprising, those four letters almost sent me to my knees. Scanning the column headed *Grades awarded*, I saw three Bs and a Z. My heart sank. I turned over the paper and read the Notes on Results. Note 2 described the grades awarded: *Z – no script submitted*. And Note 5: *If your results state you have failed, then you must re-sit all papers in the stage*. I thought I'd already accepted the reality that I would have to rewrite all four papers. But seeing it in print, dismal memories of that experience six weeks ago flooded my mind in torrents. Over the next day or so, I'd had to revert to my Emergency Kit, which, along with my new job and new friends, nursed me back from the brink of despair.

A gale of laughter breaking out around the table reeled in my thoughts. I joined in, and just then my eyes fell upon a peculiar sight. Stepping through the entryway in the distance, were two black men with whom I felt an instant connection. They looked every bit as Caribbean as me. It wouldn't have surprised me at all had they been thinking the same of me, for as they strolled past my table their eyes met mine, and instinctively our eyebrows raised and our heads nodded in mutual acknowledgement.

When, the following evening, I strode across to their table at the far end of the canteen and introduced myself, that was the start of a most peculiar friendship with these men in their mid-twenties, who turned out to be Zimbabweans.

I couldn't help feeling a tinge of guilt at having broken ranks with my clique . . . my white clique. Lying in bed one late night, I sought to justify my disaffection.

It's all this stuff on classical music, I brooded. *I just can't take any more of it. And after a hard day's work, I really don't want to discuss the performance of the FTSE 100 Share Index.* Skin colour was irrelevant. If the classical music enthusiasts had been black, yellow or green, my position would have been unchanged. In any case, I hadn't fully abandoned the Englishmen; just last week we had taken in a classical concert at the Barbican Centre which, to my surprise, I had thoroughly enjoyed.

Deep down, though, I wasn't certain I'd convinced myself that race hadn't played some little role in my decision to change tables.

The two Africans and I immediately clicked. But I soon discovered they were no more informed about the Caribbean than was the average Englishman. The young men hadn't heard of St. Lucia. Neither had they heard of the Caribbean. But they knew of Jamaica and of Bob Marley. I only half-expected the pair to know of the Caribbean's only Nobel Prize Winner – a St. Lucian, Sir Arthur Lewis, who won in economics ten years before. But they hadn't even heard of the Nobel Prize. It surprised me no end, however, that they knew of Rick Wayne, St. Lucia's famed bodybuilder, who had captured a host of international titles including Mr. Universe. Only my Zimbabwean friends thought he was British or American.

I delighted in filling in their knowledge gaps on the Caribbean's history and geography.

"Apart from us," Conrad asked in a strong Southern African accent, as we sat alone in the canteen the following evening, "are there any other coloureds in this place?"

"No, we are the only blacks here," I replied.

"Coloured!" retorted Julian, curtly.

I nodded acquiescence, unaware of the significance of the correction.

"So, what is Zimbabwe like?" I asked, still slightly rattled by the curtness in Julian's voice.

Conrad's face lit up, his voice brimming with excitement. "I tell you man, it is God's place on earth. From the Eastern Highlands to Victoria Falls, there is no better land on the face of this planet.

311

Back home we call de falls Mosi-oa-Tunya – 'the smoke that thunders'."

The short and stout young man's voice was an intense theatrical whisper as he continued. "They have a magic all of their own. When the river is high, the spray is like a towering column, and the falls make a sound like thunder. You can hear it literally miles away. There is no sight more beautiful on the planet."

I nodded, impressed. This was certainly more appealing than a critique of Beethoven's Fifth Symphony.

Conrad's dark lips were still moving. "And further downriver there are tranquil lagoons that look stunning, but you have to be constantly on the lookout for angry hippos and hungry crocodiles."

He threw his head back, roaring with laughter, his dark eyes picking up the warm glow from the chandelier above.

With equal enthusiasm, Julian joined the fray. "And the Eastern Highlands that make up our eastern border are breathtaking – three hundred kilometres of mountain range that has the Nyanga National Park in the north and the Chimanimani in the south."

"Chimanimani?" I frowned.

Julian smiled, his eyes glistening with pride, he leaned over the table. "It's what they call the other part of the mountain range. There is a small village there that holds arts festivals every year." His tone intensified, a smile slitting his lips. "But my favourite place is our capital, Harare. You'd be surprised when you see it . . . it's just like a modern European city, with lots and lots of high rise buildings and a very busy financial community that will appeal to you," Conrad chuckled.

For an instant, I felt I'd been transported back to the Caribbean, sitting with friends, taking in tall tales, jokes, and carefree laughter. Only the strange South African accent coloured the picture a different shade.

"Sounds fascinating," I smiled. "You border South Africa, right?"

"That's right," they answered in unison.

A more sombre expression crossed my face. "When I first came to London I used to work at McDonald's in the West End. One thing that always stuck in my mind was that every time I passed the South African Embassy in Trafalgar Square on my way to and from work, there were always protestors outside it demanding the release of Nelson Mandela."

Julian sighed, audibly.

"You know," I continued, "The thing that really got me was the fact that I never saw one black face among them. All the protestors were white!"

In no way was I prepared for what ensued.

"Lazy black buggers . . . they're not worth protesting for!" Conrad scowled.

"And these bloody socialists should mind their own damn business," Julian chipped in. "They have no idea what they're talking about!"

I heard the words in my head, but somehow my mind had tremendous difficulty processing them.

Julian folded his arms, his dark face twisted in disgust.

"They're wasting their time! Mandela will rot in jail!"

These words hit a wall of silence.

After the long, confused moment in which I fought a host of conflicting emotions, I could only muster a few words. "How could you guys say that?"

"The man's a criminal! A terrorist!" Julian scowled, angered, his right index finger jabbing the table. "Mandela and his ANC have killed thousands of innocent people! The man is a bloody murderer!"

I sat back, bemused, glaring across the table at the two dark-skinned men. "What's wrong with you guys? How could you say that?"

Conrad rolled his eyes, seemingly in exasperation.

Stupefied, disgusted, I said, "The man has spent twenty-five years in jail for fighting for your people!"

Julian's palm crashed down on the table with a force that exploded throughout the canteen, his mouth quivering in rage.

"Not *our* people!" he thundered. "It's the bloody blacks the bastard is fighting for! Not us!"

CHAPTER 26

Conrad placed a calming hand on his friend's forearm. He locked eyes with me. "We are not black . . . we are coloured!"

My eyes widened in bewilderment.

Conrad continued, slow, deliberate. "We are descended from the first Danish settlers in Southern Africa, who mixed with our other ancestors, the Khoi people."

He took a deep seething breath. "To be called *black* is an insult to our people."

I fixed the Zimbabwean with a fervent stare. "But surely, as far as the Apartheid South African government is concerned, any black – even one per cent black – is black. Isn't that so?"

Julian was shaking his head. "No, my friend, that's where you're wrong. It's the other way around. Any person with one per cent white is coloured, whether they look Indian, Chinese or whatever. We, the coloureds, are blessed with superior, white, genes. The whites treat us with more respect than they treat the pure Africans because the whites are part of us. This is why we have more privileges than the blacks, and it is because of this that most coloureds in South Africa, and even those in Zimbabwe, support the National Party."

After all I had heard from the two, I shouldn't have been surprised at what Julian had just said. I wasn't. I was utterly astounded. "You guys actually support the racist, apartheid, government of South Africa?"

Conrad jumped back in. "You have to understand that the blacks are lazy and uneducated, and are no better than animals."

My head shot back as if I'd just been slapped.

The short, dark-skinned man was still speaking. "It is far better to have the whites in power than the blacks."

As I listened in disbelief, a most unexpected feeling washed over me. I found myself longing for the company of my aristocratic English friends. A discourse on the delights of Beethoven's Fifth would be a welcome relief from the words spewing out of the mouths of the two Africans.

I shook my head, slowly. "People are people, regardless of skin colour."

Julian exhaled, unmistakably annoyed, his tone seething, his eyes piercing. "I am telling you this so you will understand. You have never lived where we live, so you are ignorant of the facts. We are just trying to educate you . . . my friend."

My eyes studied the two men before me: Conrad

was several shades darker than Mandela; Julian was just a shade lighter. I wasn't certain whether to feel angry at, or sorry for, the two misguided souls.

I had no way of knowing worse was yet to come.

"You know, we spent four years in the South African army fighting against the ANC," Conrad blurted.

An ominous chill raked my flesh. My words came quickly. "You guys fought against the African National Congress?"

"Yes, and we have first-hand knowledge of what those guys are capable of," Julian said. "They are not a peaceful bunch, as they would have the world believe. We found these terrorists planning to blow up a shopping mall, where families, including women and children, would have been killed. Tell that to the people protesting for the release of Mandela."

I took a deep breath, trying to calm myself, still dumbfounded, but feeling strangely drawn in, curious. "So . . . what type of soldiers were you?"

"I was an intelligence expert," Conrad said haughtily.

"I was a specialist in ambush and counter-insurgency," Julian said. "I used to carry a dagger for my job – in fact I still have it. I feel naked without it."

A devilish smile quirking his lips, Julian looked about him suspiciously, reached down to his ankles, glanced over his shoulder quickly, and then, grinning, held up a long leather-cased knife. He winked at me, then returned the weapon to its hiding place.

I arched my eyebrows, intrigued.

Julian folded his arms across his chest, looking pleased with himself. "We both knew spies who had been planted in the ANC so that we could find out what the bastards were up to."

He hesitated a moment, then shaking his head ruefully, said, "I tell you, those black bastards are a greedy and traitorous bunch. Bribing them for sensitive information was the easiest thing to do . . . they would sell their mothers and children for a few dollars if they have to."

I was cynical. I hoped my face showed it.

Conrad's eyes glared at me. "Have you ever considered how five million whites can rule twenty five million blacks? How could that be possible if the whites were not far superior?"

Before I had time to frame a response, Julian's voice cut through. "Because blacks are stupid lazy bastards."

"I'm telling you," Conrad said, "They are no better than animals. In our part of Zimbabwe and in South Africa, no one cares if you kill a black. If you see one of those Kaffirs dying by the roadside, it's like seeing a dog with its guts hanging out after it's been hit by a car. Of course, you feel sorry for it, but not sorry enough go out of your way to help it."

Despite the relative warmth of the canteen, the words chilled me. Astounded, I looked quizzically at the two decent-looking young men. My face would probably have carried the same expression had I been listening to one who argued passionately that Jesus was in fact, the son of Satan.

"I remember my uncle killing one," Julian said, shoulders shaking with mirth, his eyes glinting with amusement. "He stabbed it in its gut and it sounded like a punctured tyre . . . it went 'poof'!"

He threw back his head and shouted with laughter, Conrad joined in, and the two Africans all but collapsed across the table, roaring, screaming, shaking with laughter.

I stared at them, astounded.

When they finally succeeded in stopping their shoulders from shaking, and after the storm of laughter had dwindled into fits of helpless giggles that soon faded to empty silence, Julian said, clearing his throat, "Anyway, you too are not black," he declared. "How could you be black with a job like that? How could you be black with such a lovely complexion?"

He leaned back in his seat, a sly smile forming at the corners of his mouth, "You, my friend, are much farther up the tree of evolution."

A grin spread across Conrad's face. "You . . . my friend . . . are coloured."

CHAPTER 27

We agreed to disagree.

To me, one per cent black was black. To the Zimbabweans, one per cent white was coloured. We would never see eye to eye on this.

But still I sat with them. Still I enjoyed their company, for beneath the racist veneer I found intelligent men, fun-loving men, men I could easily relate to. Despite all that I knew about the two Africans, I somehow felt strangely drawn to them.

Did I know myself at all?

It was only the morning after I'd danced the night away at a Zimbabwean party – amid a kaleidoscope of coloured people – that my mind began to tumble with conflicts. I felt guilt nagging at me like a miserable spouse, guilt that by attending the party, I might have unwittingly endorsed the racist philosophy of the coloureds.

The struggle continued to play itself out in my mind until one Saturday afternoon, when it all came to a head.

The canteen had only a handful of patrons sitting at tables here and there. I had only a moment ago complimented the chef on the excellent smoked salmon, when from across my table I heard words that gave me pause.

"What is this *black* doing here?" Conrad stressed the word 'black', pronouncing 'a' as 'e', his voice filled with intense loathing, as though something sub-human had just crawled through the doorway.

Julian craned his head, asking hastily, "Where? Where?"

Following Conrad's line of vision, my curious eyes spotted a tall, slim, quite dark-skinned young man ambling towards our table down the aisle that led to the buffet. Instantly, I could tell he was African. He resembled a Kenyan long-distance runner. He wore a red jumper and black track pants.

My eyes shifted back to my companions around the table. Their demeanor seemed suddenly ominous, faces twisted in disgust, eyes burning with rage. I was amazed by the silent and instantaneous onrush of unprovoked hostility.

"You know this guy?" I asked, incredulous.

"No, but the kaffir is from one of the villages in Zimbabwe," said Julian hastily, his eyes riveting on the approaching man, as Conrad began to fidget in his seat.

'Kaffir', I had earlier learned, was a taboo Southern African term for black . . . not unlike 'nigger'.

"How do you know?" I probed further.

"We just know." Conrad's voice was clipped, final, dismissive. He had shifted forwards in his chair so that he was perched on the very edge, tense as though poised for swift action.

As the dark-skinned man came to within a few feet of our table, his dark eyes shifted, like the needle of a compass, to my companions. It was as if the native African had sensed he was approaching the enemy – an enemy he had spotted from a distance; an enemy he was minded to be wary of.

Their eyes locked. Conrad's glare intensified with blatant loathing. Julian's dark eyes, smouldering, were tracking the native African like a leopard stalking prey it sensed was isolated from the herd . . . waiting to pounce. Their expressions were so exaggeratedly hate-filled that I would have been amused had I not been so utterly flabbergasted. Tension hung heavy in the air.

From my seat around the table, I watched the scene unfold as if in slow motion. The meal I had so thoroughly enjoyed minutes before now soured in my stomach. I felt sympathy for the African. He had done nothing. His colour – just a darker shade of black – had offended my two companions. It made no sense.

Eyes spoke their language. I watched, I read.

How dare you place yourself in the same room as me – you black bastard! Didn't you see me here? Conrad's eyes seemed to say.

This is not home, man . . . we are equal here, said the eyes of the native African, quietly, apprehensively.

Never! . . . You animal! . . . Leave my sight forth-with, before I make you pay for your audacity!

This is England . . . we're in a public place; you can't touch me here.

You better not let me catch you later!

Come on, man. This is not called for . . . we are fellow countrymen away from home . . . let us leave the fighting for when we get back home . . . let us be at peace . . . just for now. I don't want any trouble.

As the tall, thin man passed, somewhat cautiously, our table, I detected the faintest of smiles flickering across his face – a submissive gesture.

I tried to catch the dark eyes to communicate my sorrow, my sympathy, wondering whether the poor man had seen me as one of the enemy. I had no way of knowing. The dark eyes had seen enough . . . they now looked straight ahead.

Julian and Conrad were fuming, muttering under their breaths obscenities at the man they claimed to be their compatriot . . . even after he had long passed.

I was horrified. Never before had I witnessed such an unprovoked display of venom.

I wasn't quite sure what to do next – whether to allow my eyes to reveal my extreme displeasure at what I'd just witnessed, or whether simply to feel sorry for the misguided souls, victims of racist indoctrination, victims of 'divide and rule'.

One thing I knew for sure: I was seated around a table with the coloured Zimbabweans for the last time.

CHAPTER 28

For some unfathomable reason, I awoke the next day with an overwhelming desire to do something I hadn't found the time to do in quite a while. The little voice in my head told me it was time to take another trip to Speakers' Corner. Whether this had anything to do with yesterday's experience with the Africans, or not, I simply couldn't tell.

But with my finals fast approaching, I didn't have much time on my hands. So, with only an hour or so to spare that Sunday, I quite naturally gravitated to the largest crowd. A heavy-set, learned-looking black man garbed in a flowing African dashiki stood on a soap-box under a lamp-post. Sweating profusely in the relatively coolness of the early-spring afternoon, he remonstrated with his mainly white audience massed before him.

"For four hundred years!" he bellowed, "Our people were held in bondage, against their will! Enslaved! Kidnapped from Africa! Three billion hours of free labour!"

With the powerful intonation of Dr. Martin Luther King, and the accent of a Jamaican, the man's voice resonated in the wide open space.

"With the massive profits derived from your exploitation of my ancestors, you built your vast empire! The so-called delights of London! Tower Bridge! Parliament! Big Ben! Westminster Abbey! These were all products of the wealth made out of the sufferings and groans of my ancestors!"

The bespectacled man paused, fished out a white rag from under his dashiki, and slowly dabbed his face, all the while unsmiling, surveying the sea of curious faces before him.

Then he bellowed. "I dare you to find a brick in this city which has not been cemented with the blood of an African slave!"

As I tossed and turned in bed later that evening, the speaker's words haunted me. Never before had I pondered the commercial implications of slavery. At school, my interest in the slave issue had been merely the social and emotional aspects of the great injustice – the suffering, the inequity, the deprivation, the brutality of it all.

Within me, the speaker had awakened a new consciousness. I wondered whether I would have made the trip to Hyde Park had it not been for yesterday's experience with my African friends.

I left work earlier than the usual seven pm the next day. Half hour later I was rooted in front of the Black History section of Foyles bookshop on

Charing Cross Road. Peering through volumes, I eventually spotted, on a packed bottom shelf, the thin spine of a book entitled *Capitalism and Slavery*. Instantly I recognised the author, Dr Eric Williams, the late Prime Minister of Trinidad and Tobago.

I sat on a foot-step in the brightly lit aisle between the towering bookshelves, and thumbed through the pages. It wasn't long before I suspected yesterday's speaker at Hyde Park Corner might have been influenced somewhat by Dr. William's writings.

Capitalism and Slavery, according to the preface, examined the contribution of slavery to the development of British capitalism, and in particular its role in providing the capital that funded the industrial revolution in England. Williams, then at Howard University in Washington DC, received grants from various sources to finance extensive research from historical documents dug up at the British Museum, the Public Records Office and the Bank of England Records. Upon returning to his native Trinidad, the historian entered the political arena. In 1962 he led his country to independence from Britain, becoming Trinidad and Tobago's first prime minister, a position he held until his death in 1981.

When later, a little before midnight, I set aside my accounting text and picked up *Capitalism and Slavery*, I intended merely to glance through the book before retiring to bed.

I simply could not put it down.

Lying on my stomach on my narrow bed, wide-eyed, I read and read the startling revelations. Leading merchant banks, insurance companies, the Anglican Church, British aristocracy, London, Bristol, Liverpool, Manchester, Glasgow, were all implicated in profiteering from the trade in and exploitation of African slaves.

Feeling a deep frown creasing my forehead, I read of two members of a Quaker family. David and Alexander Barclay were among the most influential merchants of their time, having profited immensely from trading in slaves in the mid-eighteenth century. Soon after, both the Barclays had married into the banking families of Gurney and Freame, and one of today's leading banks was conceived: Barclays Bank.

"My bank," I whispered in disbelief, as I reached across to the little side-table for my mug, taking a sip of cold black coffee, its aroma filling the room.

But Dr. Williams also fingered other prominent banks for accepting African slaves as loan security. These financial institutions seldom hesitated to cease their human collateral and put them up for sale on the open slave market to recover their investments.

Dr. William's revelations startled me. When slavery was abolished former slave owners received huge monetary compensation from the British Government for each slave they set free. But not a penny did the former slaves receive – three billion hours of free labour had indeed gone unpaid, but not a penny of back-pay went to the ex-slaves.

Sitting up in bed now, I felt the beginnings of bitter indignation over the great injustices that the historian so eloquently revealed. But I also felt a twinge of guilt, for it was many years ago that I learned that I carried in my veins the blood of a wealthy white plantation owner who lived in St. Vincent in the eighteenth century. Richard Gurley, a Scotsman, had fathered several slave offspring. Today, his descendents could be found in several Caribbean countries, but primarily in St. Vincent and the Grenadines . . . the birthplace of my grandfather.

But there were also Gurleys without a trace of white blood, descendants of Gurley's slaves, for slave masters attached their own names to their human chattels.

As I read on, absorbed, under the warm glow of a standing desk-lamp, mug in hand, the aroma of percolated coffee filled my single room. Outside I heard the bustle of a restless city; a city oblivious of its past. I found myself wondering about Big Ben, about Westminster Abbey, about the Houses of Parliament, and whether these imperial monuments would have existed at all had the Africans not been enslaved.

Dr. William's dissertation seemed well balanced, though, highlighting the heroics of Great British humanitarians, bold and courageous men like Wilberforce and Clarkson; men who, at great personal risk and sacrifice, had championed the emancipation of the slaves.

My eyes widened, and I felt a shiver ripple through me as I read of a debate that took place on the morality of slavery during the British General Elections of 1831. To highlight the plight of West Indian slaves, throughout the debate the humanitarians paraded up and down the hall with Negroes bound in golden chains.

The abolitionists then stepped up the campaign when they plastered, all over Britain, full-length posters of white planters flogging Negro women; when they promoted the boycott of slave-grown produce; when they secured the support of British women and children in protesting against the cruelty of slavery. The abolitionists won their victory in the end, as the British public threw their support behind the cause of emancipation.

I put down the book and tried to sleep. But the sun poured in through my glass-paned window.

I had read all night.

When I found myself making regular visits to Foyles, seeking books on black history, I realized that I had changed. I was no longer the same.

My quest to uncover the past was surpassed only by preparations for retaking my finals, and by performance on the job.

An accountant with an over-zealous interest in black history, but without the slightest inclination towards electoral politics, I often wondered where I was headed, with the bank of historical facts I carried around in my head. The future I'd foretold in front of my classmates eight years before – the belief that I was destined for a major finance job in the electricity or the telephone company back home, in no way pointed to a role that would accommodate my knowledge of the past.

But I had no way of knowing what awaited me along the long and winding road called the Future.

The Future

CHAPTER 29

Like a fleeting memory, the 1990s had come and gone in a blur.

Nelson Mandela had walked out through the gates of Robben Island prison and, like Moses, had set his captive people free. Saddam Hussein had done the unthinkable and invaded Kuwait, incurring the wrath of the Americans who had stormed into the desert to liberate Iraq's tiny neighbour.

The debate that had waged whether the year 2000 was *really* the start of the new millennium or not, had been of little consequence to me. Far more pressing matters had occupied my mind. It was with a certain sense of foreboding that I'd spent the last few hours of the old millennium and the first few hours of the new pacing my office floor, for, despite a well-planned and executed million-dollar Y2K project, I hoped and prayed the ominous Millennium Bug wouldn't bite, sparing the world the much debated and predicted global catastrophe.

In the end the Bug spewed the venom of a beetle.

Power stations didn't shut down; computer and telecommunications systems didn't crash; planes didn't fall out of the sky. Businesses remained in business; governments remained in power; the Earth remained spinning on its axis.

Now, two weeks after the 9/11 terrorist attacks in the US, I found myself seated alone at the executive desk in my office, in the colonial-style building on the Carenage in St. Georges. It was a quiet Friday afternoon in the capital of Grenada – the 'Spice Isle of the Caribbean'.

It was in this very same position, in this very same office that I'd sat on the morning of 11th September 2001, eyes transfixed on the fourteen-inch television screen on my credenza desk. In horrified silence, I'd viewed the images of the unprecedented carnage unfolding on CNN.

When I witnessed the jet slamming into the south tower of the World Trade Center, exploding into a huge fireball; when I watched, aghast, the towers crumbling to the ground, reduced to rubble, I didn't realize then the profound impact the images would have on me. Since then, like many who had witnessed the carnage, it had been, for me, sleepless nights, anxiety spells, and flashbacks of desperate souls leaping off buildings. But the ghastly images of mutilated body parts making the rounds on the internet had probably done me more harm than had the live CNN images. How I regretted opening those morbid e-mail attachments.

As I shifted in my seat, I glimpsed my reflection

in the tinted-glass window to my right. The pensive, somewhat chubby face of a thirty-seven-year-old man stared back at me. The pencil-thin moustache adjoining the thin, trimmed goatee did little to conceal the double chin in its early stages. I smiled dryly as I let my hands drop to feel the slight bulge of my mid-section.

I need to lose some weight . . . I really need to get back to the gym. It wasn't the first time I'd whispered those words to myself. But yet again, I didn't say when. I didn't *know* when.

I'd long since learned that living in paradise in no way guaranteed time to bask in the sunshine. My complexion had, over the years, stubbornly remained a sun-deprived yellow. It was little wonder my friends remained convinced that somewhere within me I carried a trace of oriental DNA – my epicanthic eye-folds, my almond-shaped eyes, perhaps betraying some long-held family secret.

As a semi-reprieve from the constriction of the office dress code, I had recently introduced 'Casual Friday', which explained why I was wearing an orange polo shirt that bore, on the breast pocket, my employer's logo – a blue digital globe.

Leaning back in my seat, legs crossed at the ankles, right thumb tucked into the pocket of my black slacks, my eyes glided upwards to the wood-framed certificates adorning the left lateral wall of the long rectangular office. As I did from time to time during moments of repose, I half-smiled up at the framed documents, allowing myself a private moment of pride.

It was with some measure of satisfaction that I regarded my status as a Fellow Chartered Management Accountant, which for me held even greater significance than my MBA from Henley Management College. My membership of the UK Institute of Directors and the Institute of Management I considered mere icing on the cake. The glass-encased certificates, arranged in a diagonal cross along the wall, were a constant reminder of my struggles in the UK and of the distance I'd travelled since that fateful day in Nottingham, when I'd absentmindedly and blissfully left the examination hall with my answer-booklet tucked away in my briefcase. But by now, in more ways than one, the silver lining of that fateful cloud had surely revealed itself.

Basking in the warm glow of my thoughts, I felt a mild smile stretching my lips, the events of 9/11 fast receding into the deepest recesses of my mind.

As my gaze shifted leftwards across my desk, I felt a surge of pride and pleasure when my eyes fell upon the ornate structure rising from the floor. The elaborate three-foot standing trophy had followed me from St. Lucia. The small rectangular plaque on its base bore the inscription:

Rudy Gurley, Executive of the Year
Awarded by the
National Secretaries Association of St. Lucia, 1994

After a minute or so of self indulgence, I shifted my focus onto the glass plaque next to the Dell computer on my desk. The words of the poem engraved on the plaque had been my steady companion since age ten, burnt into my memory by my primary-school headmaster:

> The heights that great men reached and kept
> Were not attained by sudden flight,
> But they, whilst their companions slept,
> Were toiling onwards through the night.

I strained a smile as I reflected on how literally the words of the poem had etched itself into my *modus operandi*. Over the years, my life had remained one of unrelenting toil – day and night. Having left my office at one this morning, I was surprised I hadn't yet begun to succumb to the debilitating fatigue that so often followed less than four hours' sleep. It probably helped that, being Friday, the tradition in Grenada was such that the commercial sector closed its doors by three o'clock. The rest of the day I had to myself.

Ignoring the low buzz emanating from the digital phone on my desk, I rose to my feet and, deep in thought, strolled across the carpeted floor to the bookcase standing tall against the centre of the left lateral wall. The tattered paperback that I retrieved off the packed top shelf bore a portrait of a late-middle-aged white man on the cover.

Thumbing through the book, I settled on page one hundred and twenty. In a whisper, I read:

A major key to success in this life, at attaining that which you deeply desire, is to become completely released and to throw all there is of yourself into your job or any project in which you are engaged. In other words, whatever you are doing, give it all you've got. Give every bit of yourself. Hold nothing back.

Norman Vincent Peale's positive thinking had guided me along life's uncertain journey. But of late, and all the more so after 9/11, I found myself increasingly influenced by Christopher Morley's maxim: 'There is only one success . . . to be able to spend your life in your own way'.

I had some way yet to go in achieving that one success.

As I returned *The Power of Positive Thinking* to its position in the middle of the top shelf, my eyes were drawn to the thin red and purple spine of a book tucked away on the shelf below. *Capitalism and Slavery*, that masterpiece by Dr. Eric Williams, had done much to educate me about the legacy of African slavery and its impact on life as we know it today. A firm believer in the adage that those who forget history are doomed to repeat the mistakes of the past, I vowed silently to do all within my power, some day, to bring to the world the works of the great Caribbean historian.

Rooted in front of the bookcase, my mind fleetingly returned to the catastrophic events of two weeks ago. It wouldn't have been the first time that I'd found myself pondering whether there were lessons in history that could have averted the September 11 attacks, the first foreign attack on US soil since the War of Independence.

Yet again, the answer deluded me.

The familiar low drone of a conch shell being blown outside my window drew my attention. Still deep in thought, I strolled across the floor to the large glass-paned window and gazed out upon the picturesque natural deep-water harbour of St. Georges, the afternoon sun blazing, glistening off the tranquil expanse of water. My eyes touched down on the colourful wooden canoe across the road in the water, mere yards from where I stood. The boat's yellow, green and red horizontal stripes perhaps advertising the religion of its sole occupant: a slim dark-skinned, bearded man, his long, matted copper-toned dreadlocks stiff against his sweat-glistened shoulders. The Rastafarian stood with one foot on the bow, blowing into the large conch shell, announcing his fresh catch to passers-by on the pavement above him.

As the haunting drone resonated, and as people gathered on the waterfront above the canoe, my eyes drifted out across the wide expanse of turquoise water reflecting the picture-perfect, cloudless, blue sky, to the colossal cruise ship berthed some distance out in the harbour. The floating hotels plying the tranquil waters of the Caribbean brought much-needed tourist dollars to islands whose once-vibrant agricultural industries had been decimated by the forces of globalisation.

Peering out at the faint backdrop in the distance, my eyes picked up a landscape many considered among the most beautiful white-sand beaches in the Caribbean – Grand Anse Beach.

As a Caribbean man whose grandmother and great-grandmother had been Grenadian, I felt blessed to be in Grenada, occupying an office that boasted – according to my predecessor – one of the most scenic corporate views anywhere in the world. I felt even more blessed to occupy, at a subsidiary of one of the world's most global telecommunications companies, C&W – the position of general manager.

My prediction of twenty years earlier, in front of Mrs Adrian's class, had been more than fulfilled.

CHAPTER 30

I stood by the window of my air-conditioned office, filled with a piercing sweetness and profound gratitude for God's divine intervention and guidance along that long and winding road. I gazed out upon the breathtaking scenery, reflecting on the events that had brought me to my current station in life.

When the British Airways plane had touched down at St. Lucia's Hewanorra International Airport, on the blisteringly hot afternoon of 3rd January 1991 – six years to the day since I'd left for England – I was keen to assume my senior auditor position at the Ministry of Communications and Works. The unsolicited offer from the Government of St. Lucia was timely, coinciding with my decision to return home.

Six months later, my 1981 prediction came to fruition when I accepted the position of management accountant at the local unit of the British telecommunications giant, C&W. Set up by the

British government over a century ago to provide telecommunications services to former colonies of the British Empire, C&W was the sole telephone outfit in the English-speaking Caribbean.

Following Norman Vincent Peale's advice totally and absolutely, I'd immersed myself in my work. Although I'd ascended through the middle ranks, reaching the top finance job seemed as daunting a task as climbing Mount Everest, for sitting in the financial controller's chair was a British expatriate accountant.

Over the years I'd noted the tendency for expatriates posted to the Caribbean to seek to become permanent fixtures in the sun-drenched islands. Hardly surprising, given tax-free salaries, plush accommodation, club-class travel – to mention but a few of the benefits.

Those of us ambitious West Indians who aspired to ascend the ranks of colonially-rooted companies, had long since concluded that we needed to be twice as good as equally qualified expatriates to be considered for equivalent roles.

Work-permit regulations required suitably qualified locals to be identified and groomed for expatriate-held positions. Somehow, foreign owned companies seemed always able to find loopholes to wriggle their way out of that requirement. It was with no little admiration that I observed that Barbados, a hundred miles due east of St. Lucia, insisted and ensured that top jobs were held by competent, qualified Barbadians.

When I began to come under intense pressure from the financial controller for me to relocate overseas to some unspecified job in some unspecified location, I viewed this as a surreptitious attempt to remove me, the potential local successor, and to secure the longevity of the incumbent accountant. It was at that point that I found a solution within my control.

After two years of intensively beating the books via distance learning while holding down the demanding accounts manager's job, I graduated with an MBA from Henley Management College. Three months later, the financial controller's chair was mine. That was in 1998.

A year earlier, Kenny Anthony's Labour Party had swept the polls on a ticket of good governance, transparency, and constitutional reform. I was honoured when the Prime Minister appointed me Deputy Chairman of the St. Lucia Development Bank, and Chairman a year later. I was delighted to assume leadership of the institution that had made it possible for me – through their grant of a loan secured only by the guarantee of my aunt and sister – to pursue my studies in the UK.

When some months later I was appointed to the board of directors of the National Commercial Bank of St. Lucia – after it was privatised – this paved the way to merge the development and commercial banks. Thus the Bank of St. Lucia was born. The government appointed me to the board of directors, who took measures to ensure that the developmental activities of the bank weren't lost in its quest for profits.

When I was two years into the financial controller's job, the CEO of C&W's Eastern Caribbean operations invited me to apply for the advertised position of General Manager of C&W Grenada Ltd. My attempt, diplomatically, to turn down the invitation, failed. The calls kept on coming, and I felt increasingly discomfited rejecting my boss's offer of promotion – a potential career hazard.

It was around the same time that the Eastern Caribbean islands decided to break C&W's hundred-year-old monopoly, exposing the British company to competition.

Unlike St. Lucia, where C&W's exclusive license was fast approaching expiry, several other islands had licenses which guaranteed the blue chip company a competition-free environment spanning decades, in some cases. The company would put up a fierce fight to protect its interest.

It wasn't surprising that negotiations between C&W and East Caribbean countries fast approached stalemate, each side accusing the other of intransigence, each seeming to stand like blocks of concrete, immovable. Then a seismic shift occurred when, allegedly, Calixte George, leader of the Eastern Caribbean negotiating team, and St. Lucia's Minister of Communications, accused a C&W female executive – a Trinidadian, involved in the negotiations – of being a 'house slave'.

C&W would have none of it.

St. Lucia's sole telecommunications provider for over a century decided to pack up and leave. It wouldn't seek to renew its license. Calixte George had laid on the last straw that had broken the camel's back. The island would be stranded, isolated; a telecommunications shut-down; a shut-down of economic activity; a shut-down of the country. An embarrassment to the government and the people of St. Lucia.

It was about a month or so before the company's threat to pull out that I received the call from C&W's East Caribbean CEO, asking me to apply for the position in Grenada.

Some pundits considered the company's threat merely a bluff, a negotiating strategy; the Brits would never pull out. Yet others considered it more than just a threat; C&W was using an age-old colonial manipulative technique – divide and rule. When it closed shop in St. Lucia, the other islands would cower into submission; St. Lucia was merely the sacrificial lamb, the pundits said.

I was caught in the middle and, it was then that I had considered resigning.

A friend warned me not to be a martyr.

I wasn't into martyrdom, but I disagreed vehemently with the company's stance.

This wasn't, to me, the way to end a hundred-year-old relationship; not the way to say goodbye to an old friend from whom you had profited immensely.

How could I abandon my country in such a moment of crisis? How could I fly off to new, personally lucrative pastures, when the land where my navel string was buried stood potentially on the brink of ruin?

No way was I willing to abscond at a time like this. But neither could I be disloyal to my employer. As long as the telecommunications giant remained my employer, it would be with unreserved loyalty that I performed my duties. My career had been built on a solid foundation of ethics, and right through to the end would I continue to strengthen that foundation.

When I met with Dr. Anthony to discuss my plans to quit C&W, I was more than a little impressed with the impartial advice he bestowed. The prime minister said in a voice heavy with sincerity:

"Rudy, I think your best bet is to accept the Grenada job. It's really a great opportunity for you. From Grenada, you could monitor developments at home, and if it turned out that negotiations failed to change C&W's heart about abandoning the country, it will then be up to you to decide on your next course of action. Then you could consider resigning and returning home to assist in setting up and managing the entity that would take over C&W's operations . . ."

It was soon thereafter that I took up my duties in the 'Spice Isle'. Over the ensuing few weeks, I watched, dismayed, as C&W continued its plans to leave St. Lucia. Talk continued to make the rounds in certain quarters that C&W had pulled out its man ahead of its planned withdrawal from the island.

It was only when Jamaican Errald Miller, former president of C&W Jamaica, was appointed CEO of Caribbean operations – the first West Indian so appointed – that events took a turn for the better.

But this was after the Eastern Caribbean islands had closed ranks.

"Leave St. Lucia and be prepared to leave us all,' was the message the governments so eloquently delivered.

And the company got the message. The parties agreed to return to the negotiating table. C&W withdrew its threat to leave St. Lucia.

During the first week of my posting to Grenada, C&W appointed me to its negotiating team. I led the working group responsible for negotiating with the Eastern Caribbean, a framework for telephone rates before and after competition.

CHAPTER 31

The abrupt screeching of car tires outside my window pulled me back from my thoughts. Relieved there was no follow-up bang, my eyes found the wall clock. It had just gone past four thirty. I still had some time to kill. It would be yet another hour before her plane touched down.

I made my way back across the floor, and took a seat behind my desk. My gaze alighted on the silver-framed photo standing next to the wire in-tray on the desk. The smiling face of a beautiful lady greeted me, her long jet-black curly hair, accentuated by dimpled cheeks and sparkling dark eyes making her all the more stunning. Leaning back in my seat, a slight smile revealed the inner joy that was glowing through me. It was more than the joy one occasionally felt at the sight of someone extremely pleasing to the eyes. It was the joy you feel knowing that that extremely pleasing someone is *your* special someone.

Once more, my mind travelled back in time.

The afternoon of 3rd January 1991 was hot and sunny and breezy. Ivan, my closest friend, was behind the wheel of the Marina as it sped away from the Hewanorra International Airport where, half an hour before, my flight from the UK had touched down. Soon we were enjoying coastal sites that brought back fond memories, but there was more that my eyes longed to see.

Susanna and I hadn't laid eyes on each other since my last day at the SDA Academy back in 1983, and I owed her a letter – a response to one she'd written in 1985. Naturally, therefore, when I asked Ivan to bypass the house my aunt had rented in LaClery and head northwards to Marisule, I wasn't at all surprised that I could almost hear my heart beating in my chest . . . louder and louder as we got nearer and nearer.

I'd never been to Susanna's home, but I was certain this was where she lived: second left turn up Choc Hill, just after a tire-repair shop whose business sign comprised a thin pole onto which two tires painted white were nailed.

Susanna would be surprised to see me . . . pleasantly so, I hoped.

What if she had a . . . . ?

I refused to follow the thought down to its final conclusion. It wasn't worth thinking. Destiny was destiny. Destiny would conspire to bring me that which my heart desired. So I thought.

As we pulled up at the black wrought-iron gate, the first thing that intimidated me was the grandeur of the house. Never before had I seen one bigger in St. Lucia. The second was the slim, dark-skinned, late-middle-aged Indian man who stood, green hosepipe in hand, seemingly – just like the Nottingham policeman – uninterested in winning any hospitality awards. He made no attempt to conceal his irritation – almost contempt – at the light-skinned boy who had the temerity to enter his gate, wanting to see *his* daughter.

"What do you want to see her for?"

Not exactly a question. Judging from his tone, and the way his face soured after I'd replied that I was an old school friend who'd just returned from England, and wanted to say hi, he might as well have shouted at me to get out of his yard.

When I glanced up and saw Susanna's enquiring face staring down at me from the balcony, I felt my heart jolt in my chest as if my foot had bumped a rock across my path. She was gorgeous. She had done something to her hair.

Then I saw her expression. Feeling a light drizzle wetting my face, I knew then, that I had seen the third thing that intimidated me that late afternoon. It was the look . . . the look you instinctively would give to a stranger who'd just invaded your space – an unmistakeable look of annoyance. I had more than invaded Susanna's space. I had shown up at her doorstep un-announced, and she wanted to know who was this chubby, light-skinned young man, who seemed so bold and so blissfully unaware of her over-protective father lurking somewhere in the shadows. Her father's reaction had caught me off-guard, and I felt somewhat nettled.

It was when Susanna's eyes touched down on Ivan – her former classmate – that she flung a searching glance at me.

"Gurley, is that you?" she asked from the balcony above, her voice slightly nasal.

I smiled.

She did not.

"I didn't know you were in St. Lucia."

"I'm not . . . I mean I wasn't . . . I just came in."

"You could come up . . . it's raining," she said after a moment's hesitation.

"Gosh, you look shorter and a bit fat . . . that's not how I remember you," she said casually, as we approached the top landing.

She reached out to shake my outstretched hand. "My! . . . look at your rosy cheeks."

The look that crossed her face wasn't quite a smile; it was more a look of stunned amusement.

I felt my face growing hotter by the second.

Moments later, perhaps to even the score, I heard myself asking about her hair – what had she done to it? It looked different. When Susanna replied, I had to stop myself from asking why she needed to relax her beautiful curly hair . . . that this wasn't at all necessary.

As the three of us sat on the cosy sofa on the large balcony overlooking the blue waters of Choc Bay and Rat Island in the distance – a stunning panoramic view – I was surprised how relieved I felt when Susanna mentioned she was suffering a bout of flu. It was the first time I'd taken such comfort in another's misfortune. Only then did I begin to feel my nerves calming, believing the virus, and nothing else, to have been responsible for her seemingly icy reception. The dream was still alive, I thought.

As my heartbeat regained some semblance of normalcy, and as my eyes studied her face, I realised that in the six years I'd spent in England, never had I encountered a woman I considered half as lovely as Susanna. Clad in a simple but well-fitting house dress, her long, now-straightened hair, fell loosely and somewhat waywardly about her shoulders, with little feathery, curly wisps clinging around her temples. The fact that she had the flu in no way detracted from her beauty. I found myself thinking that her fine bone structure ensured Susanna was a woman who would look lovely at any age. Her large, dark eyes, though slightly reddened by her ailment, revealed an indefinable magnetism that somehow held me captivated, entranced, entranced by the aura that made her look seductive yet untouchable, virginal yet sensual.

Her voice was steady, with a gentle even pitch, as she explained that since leaving school in 1985 she'd been employed at the family business. Working in every conceivable position – from the factory floor to the office, she was now the company's admin manager. The devout Christian had remained true to her faith and was deep into the church and her music, being a lead singer of a gospel group.

As I listened to the voice of the girl, who, ten years before, I'd declared would someday wear my ring, I sensed beneath the sophisticated beauty, beneath her gentle demeanour, an inner fortitude that somewhat surprised me. No longer was she that shy little girl I had so clumsily approached at the school entrance that sunny afternoon, ten years before . . . the thirteen-year-old who once told me her mother said she couldn't have a boyfriend before leaving school.

She'd left school . . . I wondered . . .

Again, as quickly as it entered, I cast out the thought – destiny was destiny.

As the three of us chatted away for all of thirty-five blissful minutes, in no way did I suspect that that deep conviction, that that strong-willed personality, that indomitable spirit, that that deep religious devotion that I saw in Susanna, would cause me no end of difficulty over the next four years, as I tried desperately and in vain, to impose my will upon her. Her Christian principles were not up for sale. She refused to . . .

I jumped in my seat, startled by the sudden vibration emanating from around my waist. I had all but forgotten the cell phone clipped to my belt. As I unhooked the Nokia 8650, pressed the answer key and brought the phone up to my ear, it was Susanna's voice that I heard at the distant end.

"Hi hon."

"Hi, where are you?"

"You won't believe it; I'm still in St. Lucia."

"Oh no."

"The LIAT flight is running late, we'll be leaving in the next few minutes."

"Okay, no problem. I'm just chilling in the office. You know, I was just thinking of you?"

"Really? What about?"

"Just about our history and all that, and in particular how hard a time you gave me."

"You should have gotten over that by now."

"Don't worry," I said slowly, smiling mischievously, "I'll make you pay later."

"Oh please, not on the phone."

I chuckled, not at all surprised by her reaction.

"Anyway, babes, they are calling our flight . . . have to run, see you later."

"Okay, bye."

Returning the Nokia to its case clipped to my belt, a slight smile kept teasing my lips, my mind reminding me how conservative Susanna had remained over the years. Solid and unyielding, at times much to my chagrin, she had devoutly stuck to her Christian principles.

On 23rd December 1995, after I'd suffered four years of amorous frustration, and after I'd come perilously close to giving up, we said our vows at the Holy Trinity Anglican Church. It was for me, the fulfilment of a fourteen-year-old dream, a blissful occasion with friends and family.

When earlier this year, 2001, I took up my position in Grenada, it was our need to keep our private business going that had kept my wife in St. Lucia. Recognising the desire to boost our financial independence, the year before we tied the knot we'd set up a small pasta manufacturing business, which, over the years, had grown steadily. We hoped that at some time in the future our business, Tenderoni would become our full-time vocation, our bread and butter. In the time being it remained a side operation; Susanna continued to hold down her position at the family business.

It was always with keen excitement that we looked forward to our weekends, each of which we vowed to spend together, alternating between St. Lucia and Grenada. It was Susanna's turn, today, to island-hop.

With just two more hours to play with, this late Friday afternoon, work wasn't on my list of games. I'd thoroughly enjoyed my quiet moments of deep reflection, marvelling that such tragic events as those of September 11 could inspire such profound introspection.

Life is good, I whispered, as I rocked gently back and forth in my chair, smiling, eyes closed, right fingers gently caressing my goatee, my mind a jumble of thoughts. A successful career, financially secure, married to the woman of my dreams, only little Rudys and little Susannas would complete the picture, but we had decided to wait. No doubt,

Susanna would make a great mother. I wasn't certain how good a father I would make . . . but it wouldn't be too difficult, I thought, to be better than mine had been for me. Not at all difficult, in fact – all I had to do was stay the course . . . not run away.

Sitting still now, thoughts of my brief encounter with my mother came flooding in. It was back in 1988 when I'd left Milton Keynes for Nottingham that I had last spoken to Rosemary. Our encounter wasn't altogether a resounding success, but my curiosity had at least been quelled. I could claim to have met my mother.

But my father . . . quite a different story.

During my six years in England, never had I ceased scanning faces of strangers that I passed in the streets, on buses, on the underground. I studied the faces of men fitting the scant description of the father that I didn't know – tall, light-skinned black men; strangers – bus drivers, conductors, pedestrians – I scanned their faces for clues, clues of some kinship.

A whole host of questions now hijacked my mind, as I uncrossed my legs, still leaning back in my seat, my face taut with concentration.

Where was Rodney on 9/11, at the instant the second plane slammed into the south tower? I wondered. Surely, the man must have seen the carnage, or at least would have heard about it. Like most, my father undoubtedly would have recalled his exact location at the moment of impact.

What were his thoughts then? Did he think of friends? Did he think of family? Did he think of Roslyn and me?

When was the last time we crossed his mind? Did we ever cross his mind? My mind was in overload.

Rodney had cradled my sister as a baby, but had never held me; he had never seen me. But he knew of me.

Where's Rodney? I wondered. What's become of him? Did the Barbadian make a success of his life? Or, was he, like many first-generation West Indians who had migrated to Britain, scratching out a living in some menial job, or worse yet, unemployed? How many children had he fathered? Was the man even alive?

I had long ago given up hope of ever finding my father. But now . . . this very instant, I felt an overwhelming need to find answers to the many questions hovering around in my head like ghosts.

Like a sixty-watt bulb, an idea suddenly illuminated my mind. The idea flashed around in my head, becoming clearer and clearer, until finally it became a picture. I knew what I needed to do.

Adrenalin coursing through me, my pulse quickening by the second, I swivelled my chair around to face the Dell PC on my side table.

"Everything is possible," I whispered, as I reached for the keyboard.

In the address bar I typed: *www.yahoo.com/.*

Then at the blinking cursor, I entered: *'finding lost relatives'.*

Five seconds later I had the results on the screen.

I reviewed the first ten hits from the list of 19,000 that churned out; then the next, and the next. Nothing inspiring. By the tenth, frustration was beginning to get the better of me.

Then I clicked a site that caught my attention. *'People Tracer'* promised to search over one hundred million records: electoral rolls, lifestyle databases; births, deaths, marriage records. I felt encouraged that they offered a service on a 'no results, no charge basis'. Nothing to lose, I thought.

Feeling my pulse sprinting, I entered the requested information: Rodney Greenidge, Male, Barbadian, emigrated to Britain in or around 1963.

Terms and conditions popped up on the screen. I clicked 'OK'. It will cost five hundred pounds, half due upfront. I entered the requested credit card number and expiry date.

When later that evening, I told Susanna what I had been up to, she seemed even more anxious than I.

"Now I could see what you will look like in old age," she teased after she'd reminded me of the number of times she had prompted me to launch a search for my elusive father.

"Come on, now," I replied, "late middle-age; he can't be that old."

"And I hope you call him Daddy," she said, smiling mischievously.

"Don't be silly . . . never."

After an anxious two weeks, an e-mail from *People Tracer* appeared in my inbox one morning. I felt my heart skip a beat.

With grave trepidation, I clicked the attachment. A form appeared on the screen before me.

I read:

MISSING PERSON TRACE

ENQUIRY INFORMATION

On the strength of the limited last known details, it would appear that the subject of enquiry is Rodney William Greenidge, born in around 1943.

Trace action has ascertained that he is currently residing at the following address:

80 Kinnaird Avenue
Catford
Surrey

Tel: No listing

We are informed that he resides here along with his wife, Mrs Janet Angela Greenidge. They have a son named Semeon Rodney Greenidge who was born in September 1983.

We trust that this information will be of assistance and thank you for instructing us in this matter.

REPORT END

My heart was leaping with joy, my mind humming in high gear. A surge of euphoria rippled through me, a warm, glowing feeling. I reminded myself to be cautious; cautious that this person might *not*, after all, turn out to be my long-lost father.

But my mind instantly threw caution to the wind. *To hell with it! It had to be him. It had to be Rodney.* I imagined a struggling, ageing West Indian, whose economic status was such that he couldn't afford even a telephone. The guy was obviously down and out, I mused.

Picking up my desk phone, my fingers dialled Susanna's number in St. Lucia. She picked up and listened, barely able to contain herself. I felt her excitement as I disclosed my plans.

Half an hour later, I drafted the letter Susanna and I had discussed.

Dear Mr Greenidge,

My name is Rudy Gurley – a St. Lucian currently residing in Grenada. If indeed you are the same Rodney Greenidge who migrated to the UK in the early 60s, having been involved with a St. Lucia girl by the name of Rosemary Gurley, it is very much likely that you and I are related, and I believe you may know the extent to which we are.

I've enclosed a photo of myself.

Please feel free to call me collect. My telephone no. is (473) 444-1686.

The FedEx package that I posted the next day would arrive on the suspect's doorstep in three days. I knew it would be three days of eternity.

CHAPTER 32

A full two weeks had passed since I'd written that letter. Not a word.

That early Sunday afternoon I was lounging on the pool deck with some friends who'd come over from St. Lucia. In the midst of describing to my attentive guests Grenada's turbulent past, I thought I heard the faint but persistent ringing of the telephone.

I blurted a quick excuse, hoisted myself up, leaped over a deckchair, and jogged through the patio-doors into the living room, and into my study next to the front door.

I panted into the phone. "Hello."

There was silence on the line, then: "Hello . . . can I speak to Rudy Gurley?"

The voice was unfamiliar. A male voice with a slight Barbadian cadence, somewhat refined, but slightly tremulous.

I frowned, recalling that the last time I'd received a call from Barbados on a Sunday it had been unwelcome news. All C&W Caribbean general managers

362

had fielded similar calls – a directive from head office to cut employee numbers by ten per cent.

"Rudy speaking."

I heard a quick intake of breath over the phone. It was several seconds before the refined Barbadian accent, spoke again. "Hi Rudy."

"Hi."

Another empty silence.

"I'm calling from England."

I realized I'd nodded, as if speaking to someone standing before me.

Then I heard the voice say, tremulously, "Hi Rudy . . . this is Rodney.

"Sorry?"

The Barbadian accent wavered. "This is Rodney."

I was certain I'd heard the name before. I just couldn't place it. *Rodney. Rodney. Rodney.*

Then, for some unfathomable reason, against the dead silence on the phone, my mind tuned in to the surrounding noises. From the patio I heard the distant pleading voice of a little girl asking for orange juice; I heard the loud splash of water in the pool followed immediately by the screams of young girls, then their angry voices sharp in rebuke; then, against the hammering of my heart, my ears re-tuned to the deafening silence on the telephone line, my mind recalling the letter I'd sent to the address in Surrey, England.

Rodney. Rodney Greenidge. My long-lost father is on the line?

I shuddered. Any moment now, I half expected to wake up in bed and focus my groggy eyes on

363

the bedside clock that would probably confirm I was late for work, or give me some other cause for disappointment. I hoped not. This wasn't the sort of dream from which I cared to awaken. But nothing happened. Thank God. I simply stood there in the middle of the semi-enclosed study, telephone in hand, trying to catch my bearings, feeling excitement exploding in the pit of my stomach.

I pulled up a chair and took a seat at the desk before me. Heart fluttering in my chest, I swallowed hard, pulled in a deep, fortifying breath, then spiritedly, as if to an old friend I hadn't seen in years, I said, "Hi Rodney, how are you?"

"I'm okay," said the Barbadian accent, after another seemingly awkward pause.

I found myself thinking that perhaps the voice couldn't afford the transatlantic telephone call. "Would you like me to call you back?"

"No . . . that's okay."

Visions of a downtrodden West Indian scratching out a living working the night shift of some factory, stealing a call on his employer's telephone line, flashed through my mind amid growing excitement. But something about the voice seemed to betray that image.

"So, how are you," I heard myself asking.

"I'm fine, thank you . . . I got your letter."

"Okay."

"Are you surprised to hear from me?" the Barbadian accent asked, still somewhat shakily.

"No . . . not really . . . for some strange reason

I thought you might call today." I couldn't put a finger on why I'd said that – a blatant untruth. I'd all but forgotten about that letter.

"Your note was very well written, concise and effective . . . very professional, I'd say. I was most impressed."

Both his choice of words and the educated tone in which he spoke them had me rethinking my image of the man on the other end of the line.

"Thanks."

"I've mailed you a letter in response. Have you received it yet?"

"No . . . not yet," I said, taking a long deep audible breath in the silence that followed.

"Well, it should be on its way. You should get it soon enough." He paused. "But please ignore it as this conversation supersedes it."

His tone was surprisingly refined . . . surprisingly educated. This wasn't the voice of a down-trodden man.

"You know, Rudy, I haven't slept a wink since I read your letter," the voice continued, still waveringly. "It has turned my whole world upside down . . . my life has been a living hell ever since."

"I'm sorry to hear that . . . this was not my intention."

"But I'm beginning to feel better now . . . much better."

"Good."

"The letter you will receive from me basically says that I am very sorry that I abandoned you and

365

Roslyn, but that I'm not able to face you now; that I'm not ready to deal with any resentment you may be harbouring towards me."

I was numb with shock. Not simply because of what he said, but because he actually mentioned my sister's name. I hadn't referred to her by name in my letter . . . Rodney actually remembered Roslyn's name.

"I have no resentment towards you," I said. "I have no time for this; I'm just really happy that I've finally been able to track you down. If I were resentful, I would have made no attempt to contact you."

Rodney's voice seemed to falter even more. "Rudy, you don't know how relieved I'm to hear you speak those words."

"Great."

"You know . . . I wasn't planning to call you at all, but I could bear it no longer. I just had to call . . . and I'm really, really nervous."

His voice dropped to almost a whisper. "It's about ten o'clock in England now . . . my family are asleep. I'm actually sneaking to make this call."

Rodney paused. I did not speak. He continued.

"A couple of weeks ago my wife called me at work and told me that a Fedex package addressed to me had arrived from Grenada."

I pressed the phone harder against my ear.

"When I received that call, I knew instantly that my past had caught up with me. I felt my whole world caving in on me. I couldn't work another second, and so I left my office and came home immediately.

366

He paused before continuing.

"When I arrived home, I just could not bring myself to open the letter. I stared at it for practically an entire day. I was so nervous that I really thought I was on the verge of a mental breakdown."

I listened intently, not speaking.

"Hello? Hello?" came Rodney's panicked voice.

"Yes, I'm here."

"Okay . . . sorry about that Rudy, I thought you had hung up."

"Not at all. I wouldn't do that."

"I'm really happy to hear that." He seemed to clear his throat. "This experience has been a living hell," he continued, "But ironically, Rudy, now that I'm speaking to you, it's been a living hell in the sweetest possible way."

He paused a few moments, then said, "My family didn't know about you and Roslyn."

Astounded, feeling as though caught up in some American soap opera, my words came slowly, my tone incredulous. "Really? They didn't know?"

"My family knew nothing about that part of my life. I didn't know how to tell them. I was a nervous wreck. But it was inevitable. I finally mustered the courage to tell Angela . . . my wife . . . my second wife. She knows now. She took it very, very hard. She felt hurt and betrayed."

He waited as though he expected some special reaction from me. None came. He continued. "If she wasn't a Seventh Day Adventist, I believe I would have lost her . . . and I wouldn't blame her at all."

"How does she feel now?" I asked, at the back of my mind registering that once again the SDA had played some part in my life.

"I believe she has reluctantly accepted the situation. But it's still very uncomfortable for me. I've been living a lie all those years, and I'm really ashamed of myself."

Another vacant pause. "I didn't know how to tell my sons, when I . . ."

"Sons? You have sons? How many?"

"I've got three . . . two with my wife, nineteen and seventeen years old".

"What about the third?'

Rodney seemed to hesitate a moment, then in a faltering tone, he said, "Well . . . that's you, Rudy."

I felt sheepish. I'd completely forgotten, at least for a moment, that the voice I was listening to was actually that of the man who'd donated my twenty-three chromosomes. Somehow, my mind seemed to have extracted itself from the situation. I was speaking to a long-lost friend, catching up on events in his life . . . his family . . . other people's lives. No connection to me.

"Of course," I said, my tone suggesting obviousness, a weak attempt to recover from my embarrassment.

He was still speaking. "I didn't quite know how to tell my sons, so in the end I simply showed Semeon and Garfield, your brothers, the picture you had sent me, and asked them if they knew who you were. When they said no, I simply told them it was their older brother. They were shocked."

"Understandably so," I said.

"Of course."

"How are they coping now?"

"Well, other than the fact that I'm now being accused of double standards, I believe they're okay with it now. The thing is, I'm always preaching to my kids about morals; ethics; how to conduct their lives, and so on. So now they think I'm a hypocrite. I believe the younger one is taking it a lot harder, though. When I came home from work the next day, as I walked through the front door, I heard one of Bob Marley's songs blasting away in the living room. Something about 'hypocrites and parasites'."

I couldn't hold back the chuckle welling up in my throat . . . it burst out. I pretended I'd succumbed to a fit of coughing, relieved that Rodney couldn't see my face.

In a state of all-consuming euphoria, I leaned back in my chair, pale legs stretched out over the surface of the desk in front of me.

Everything around me seemed surreal: the sun blazing from the picture-perfect blue sky, shimmering its radiance over the bay; sounds of waves breaking gently on the sandy shore bordering my garden; the gentle breeze rustling tree leaves and wafting through my study; the orchestra of exotic singing birds; the occasional crowing of roosters from somewhere in the distance; the mingled aroma of coffee, nutmegs, cherries, seaweed; the conversation

I was having with the Barbadian accent four thousand miles across the Atlantic. It all seemed surreal, and I couldn't wipe that smile off my face.

How I wished Susanna hadn't stayed in St. Lucia this weekend to attend a funeral.

Continuing to press the phone hard against my ear, listening intently, I couldn't help thinking that Rodney had made a career of keeping secrets – secrets of his shady past – secrets he had also kept from another of my siblings, a daughter, from his first marriage. She, too, Rodney confessed, had been kept in the dark all those years. It was with relief in his voice that he mentioned that on receiving the news of Roslyn's and my existence, his second daughter had seemed more intrigued than upset.

When I mentioned that Roslyn and her teenage daughter – Rodney's first and only grandchild – lived in Islington, North London, and that Roslyn was a court stenographer, I would have sworn I heard a sudden hollow crash on the other end of the line – the sound of a phone dropping to the floor. When I mentioned my sister's work address in the City of London, the ensuing silence lasted several seconds. Rodney, it turned out, worked a block or two from my sister. Father and daughter might very well have passed each other several times along the streets of London.

I couldn't begin to imagine the range of emotions he might have been experiencing as he took in the information.

At length, in a more stable tone of voice, Rodney

spoke of his life. A young man arriving in the UK in the early sixties, taken up with the metropolis, he'd made some mistakes. The youngster had hooked up with a woman he'd known from Barbados – the woman destined to be his first wife. The last time Rodney had seen his childhood sweetheart – Rosemary – that fateful day in 1964 at his apartment under the watchful gaze of a very pregnant wife, neither he nor Rosemary had mentioned Roslyn or me; Rodney had simply assumed we had accompanied Rosemary to England. It seemed to come as a surprise to him that I'd first seen my mother only after my twenty-first birthday, and that for Roslyn the meeting had been much later.

I marvelled that Rodney appeared to take refuge in the fact that for several years his address had remained unchanged, Rosemary knew, all along, where to find him. So she could have found him, if she wanted to. Fingers were beginning to point. I had no appetite for such games.

Spellbound, I listened, forgetting my guests lying leisurely around the pool, my mind partially blocking out noises of children, murmuring of adults, and uncannily, Kool and the Gang's 'Celebration', playing at a respectable decibel-level in the adjoining living room.

After driving one of those big red London buses for over a year, and after a brief spell in the British army, the young Rodney Greenidge had gone back to college, paving his way for entry into the British civil service. Now, at fifty-nine, in the twilight of a successful career – a senior officer in the Treasury, advising members of parliament on tax matters – my father was looking forward to retirement some time next year. He couldn't wait to spend more time with the family.

Over the years, it seemed the skeletons in his cupboard had ceaselessly tormented him; ghosts of the past haunting him day and night. They had set a time bomb . . . a ticking time bomb he knew would one day detonate. For years, in the deep recesses of his mind, the bomb had ticked away. Tick. Tick. Tick. In anguish, he'd listened to the ticking day and night, in the certainty that the appointed hour of detonation would one day arrive, blowing his life to smithereens. In his dreams, in his nightmares, Rodney saw faces – faces of the past: Rosemary, Sheila, Chung Li, Mother; the inno-cent, unfocused eyes of two children.

Listening to my father, I imagined the torture he must have endured, having been unable to share with his wife details of the nightmares that had awakened him so regularly, with a start, sometimes violently, sometimes in a cold sweat.

It was with no little surprise that I heard of the photograph of the little boy; the picture Rodney kept hidden away in a trunk in his attic. A photo-graph of a one-year-old boy sitting on a chair. I was smiling.

Our father also kept a picture of Roslyn; Roslyn at eighteen months, bashfully holding onto

Rosemary's dress; a picture similarly hidden away in the trunk in his attic. Another skeleton in his cupboard.

The time bomb had kept ticking away. Tick. Tick. Tick. Until last week.

But for me, the seismic shock was yet to come.

It had never occurred to me to ask about Rodney's mother and father . . . my grandparents. For some strange reason, my thoughts had never turned to them. It was with some sadness that I listened to Rodney's melancholy voice saying that his father – my grandfather – only last year, at the ripe old age of eighty-five, had passed away. All his life, my grandfather had lived in Barbados . . . all his life . . . all that time . . . on the same street, in the same house . . . the same house in which Rodney had grown up; the same address in Grazettes – the same address where my eighty-three year old grandmother *still* lived.

No sooner had I ended the marathon cross-Atlantic conversation than I had Susanna on the other end of the line. Hardly containing her excitement during the half-hour or so that we spoke, she couldn't wait to give Sheila the news.

I imagined my beaming wife hurriedly making her way across the sunny living room, past the dining area, down the flight of stairs, through my book-lined study, and into Sheila's apartment occupying the ground floor of our Cap Estate home in St. Lucia. My aunt, Sheila, who had been mother and father to me, would probably burst into tears, praising the Almighty, and proclaiming how she knew instinctively something big was about to happen . . . she had seen something in her dreams.

When, moments later, my phone rang, I knew Sheila was experiencing one of the happier moments of her not–too-happy life. And yes. She had had that dream. She had known something big would happen.

Within minutes, the news had crossed the Atlantic. My Aunt Toya of Manchester said the inevitable had happened. I knew it would be a sleepless night for Roslyn in London.

As I lay in bed later that evening, after blissfully filling my intrigued guests in on my dreamlike telephone conversation, and after we'd thoroughly enjoyed a Chinese dinner then karaoke in the private dining room at the Bamboo Village restaurant, I fared no better than my sister. My mind was buzzing. What I felt as I lay wide awake in bed was more than sheer joy. It was more a combination of bliss, rapture, tranquillity – a melding of body, mind, and spirit; a feeling that pervaded every fibre of my being. It seemed my brain had flooded my bloodstream with happy neurochemicals, and it was on an endorphin high, a natural high, that I found myself floating, as I played and replayed the events of earlier today, trying to make sense of it all.

'My grandparents had lived in Barbados all those years,' I whispered to the close-board ceiling.

My mind recalled the many meetings I'd attended in Barbados after the half-hour flight from St. Lucia; the innumerable times I'd sat in the departure lounge at the Grantley Adams International Airport, awaiting my flight to Grenada, or in transit back to St. Lucia. *All that time, my grandmother had lived in Barbados?*

I could easily have bumped into Rodney and family in the departure lounge as they awaited their British Airways flight back to England after one of their regular visits to Barbados. I could easily have bumped into my father last year on his way back from his father's funeral. Would I have recognised Rodney? Would he have recognised me? Did the thought of hopping across to St. Lucia to see his kids ever cross his mind? No . . . I forgot . . . we were meant to be living with Rosemary in England. But did he ever think of taking the thirty-five minute flight just to see, one last time, the Gurley family . . . the family he had stayed with in St. Lucia in the sixties, before leaving for England?

My attempts to reel in my thoughts as I lay in bed that night failed miserably.

The telephone conversation with my eighty-three-year-old grandmother the next day was yet another surreal experience – an experience unmatched by my visit the following Friday, to Grazettes, Barbados.

CHAPTER 33

When the white Toyota Corolla slowed to round the corner into the sprawling community of Grazettes, Barbados, I didn't think we would have to put up with fifteen more minutes of banter from the irate taxi driver. He complained bitterly, incessantly, that the street name and house number we'd given him wasn't nearly sufficient to enable him to find my grandmother's house.

He was still fuming when we eventually pulled up next to the medium-sized wall house at the top of the hill. "It don't matter that she old," he remonstrated, in a sharp Barbadian accent, "she should be able to give proper direction. Who go pay for all this petrol I burn up looking for she?"

Susanna and I were simply too distracted, too filled with anticipation, to pay the indignant man any attention. Our gazes were riveted on the little old lady standing in the doorway of the house nestled at the top right corner of the road. She was beaming, and when, from the short distance our eyes met hers, instantly, our faces spread into broad smiles.

"Keep the change," I muttered to the driver, as we climbed out of the car, my gaze hardly shifting off my grandmother, whose gleaming eyes studied our every move like a proud mother observing her toddler's early steps.

Hand in hand, smiles hovering, Susanna and I approached the old woman who looked nothing like I'd imagined. At eighty-three – well past life's contract – my grandmother's youthful appearance came as a surprise. She seemed to have aged gracefully – no geriatric tell-tale signs, no loose, heavy bags under the eyes; no deep, folding wrinkles; no pronounced stoop in her posture. Awaiting our arrival in the shade of her doorway, hidden from the scorching sun beating down upon us, her brown face radiated sheer delight.

My grandmother's embrace was firm, her cheeks soft against my lips as we greeted each other.

"Hello, Rudy," she said, her voice shaky, her slightly reddened eyes misty.

"Hi, Mrs Greenidge," I said, still locked in embrace.

These first words were no casual utterances. It was after more than an hour or so of quiet contemplation last night that I'd composed my introductory greeting. 'Grandmother', 'Grandma', 'Granny', were all candidates, but in the end, I had settled for what came naturally. 'Mrs Greenidge' had won hands down.

Gesturing towards Susanna, I said, "This is my . . ."

I never finished. The two beaming women were already hugging, exchanging kisses, greetings; making cheerful noises; noises of women delighted in meeting each other.

Broad smiles remaining on our faces, excitement rippling through me, the old woman, regal in her long floral dress, led us through a small spotless kitchen, and into a neat, comfortably furnished, medium-sized, carpeted living room.

Upon entering the room, a rather odd feeling instantly came over me. An uncanny feeling. Not quite that uncanny *déjà vu* feeling of having already seen or experienced something that was being experienced for the first time. *Nothing* was familiar about meeting my grandmother for the first time; nothing familiar about the house, the room, the experience. Nothing whatsoever. Rather, it was a feeling that it all *ought* to have been familiar. I *should* know this pleasant old woman leading us into her living room; I *should* know every nook and cranny of this house; I *should* know this living room. But I didn't. The strangeness lay in the fact that it was not familiar, when in fact it really ought to have been.

I took a seat next to Susanna on the upholstered settee. When my eyes fell upon the object standing on the centre table, I did a double-take, feeling a shiver ripple through me.

The object to which my eyes riveted was a framed photograph of me; a photograph I hadn't seen before. But in no way did I recognise the attractive dark-skinned lady whose face was wreathed in a smile as she stood next to me in an elegant wedding dress. Neither did I recognise the handsome dark suit that I wore. I didn't recognise it because it was *not* my suit. The attractive lady in white was *not* my wife.

Moving in closer, pulse racing, my eyes squinted at the picture. I blinked. I blinked again, and again. It was *not* me. It was Rodney. Rodney . . . my father.

Tall, light-skinned, narrow eyes, high cheek bones – the man in the framed picture standing on the centre table, was my mirror image. That half smile; that upright posture; that high hairline, it was all me. But it wasn't.

"Gosh," I heard Susanna exclaim, as I felt her firm grip tighten on my arm. "Rudy, this is you . . . you two could be twins!" Her voice was a quick intense whisper.

Moments later, when I felt a slight tapping on my thigh, my eyes shot down to see Susanna's hand gesturing, drawing my attention to the smiling old lady who now stood before us, tray in hand. We enjoyed the glasses of refreshing mauby she presented to us – a soft drink made from the bark of a tree, home-made from a traditional recipe. When we sat around the well-set table in the adjoining dining room, it was a special feast of rice and peas, fried flying fish, yam, dasheen, fried plantain, passion-fruit juice, and more of the refreshing mauby that I couldn't have enough of.

As we chatted through the meal, again I felt the onset of that uncanny feeling; the feeling of what should be, but wasn't. My grandmother's cooking I should be familiar with, but I wasn't.

My fork picked up the last piece of fried plantain from my plate and, tongue in cheek, it dawned on me that had we been in Japan, I would probably have burped long and loud to signify my complete satisfaction with the meal. But being in the West, where different standards of etiquette apply, I resorted instead to blurting out how delicious the food was, sentiments that my wife echoed.

The techno beat that heralded the BBC World News was pulsating from the television to the front of the room when Susanna and I settled back into the comfort of the settee. Soon we were taking in stories of Rodney, his boyhood, his adulthood – his life. One of two children – Rodney's older sister having emigrated to the States – my father had been, for the most part, a well-behaved boy, but one who nevertheless enjoyed fun and games a bit too much, according to his mother. Although excelling in most sports, it was table tennis that had propelled the youngster to the status of a national celebrity, having represented Barbados in his teens. He'd joined the British army during his early days in the UK, but it wasn't long before he regretted the decision. After he'd convinced a commanding officer that he, Rodney, was flat-footed and unfit for military service, he took to driving a London bus – a vocation his mother vehemently disapproved of.

She kept pressing her son to return to college so he could make 'something worthwhile of himself'.

"The boy eventually followed my advice," my grandmother was saying, "and after all is said and done, he has not done too badly for himself."

I couldn't help noting how articulate she seemed. She spoke with a vigour that suggested she might have been an assertive lady in her day. Somehow, I found myself wondering how different my life would have been had I known her all my days. I ought to have known her all my days. But I hadn't. That uncanny feeling again. Again, I shook it.

She was still speaking. "Rudy, when your mother became pregnant with your sister . . . with Roslyn . . . it came as a real shock to your grandfather and me, you know."

Her gaze never left my face as she continued. "Rodney was brought up as a good Christian boy, and he should have known better. We were very, very disappointed in him. It caused us a lot of embarrassment in the community, you know. After all we were a God-fearing family."

Shaking her head ruefully, she put in, "He really should have known better."

Inwardly, I chuckled at the thought that had Rodney known better, had he not broken the rules, bringing shame and disrepute upon his family, I wouldn't have been here today.

"Over the years," she went on, her voice laced with regret, "I kept telling the boy to go and look for his children in St. Lucia whenever he visited us down here in Barbados. St. Lucia isn't that far away, you know. But Rodney never listened to me . . . the boy never listens. He seemed afraid of something. I suppose we all feared that perhaps you and Roslyn had gone astray. That you were on the streets."

She hesitated a moment as if coming to an important decision, then said. "We thought that maybe you and your sister had become drug addicts or something . . . we just didn't know what to expect."

I listened, detached. It didn't seem to me that it was my sister and me being discussed. I was seated on the sideline, listening to someone else's story. Not mine. Not my family's.

Her voice shifted up a gear. "I'm so proud of you, Rudy. You've done so well . . . a big executive with C&W. I wish your grandfather was here to see you."

As a proud grandmother would, the old woman's face beamed, her eyes gleaming with delight.

"Thank you," I said. "So tell us more about Rodney." I stretched out my legs, crossed them at the ankles and, feeling the warmth of Susanna's hand in mine, leaned back, expectantly.

More tales unfolded.

I felt suspended in a warm glow of euphoria. Eloquently, my grandmother spoke as though, over and over again in her mind, she had rehearsed what she would say, and something about the way she spoke the words left that warm fuzzy feeling deep within me.

When she mentioned the gift she had sent to St.

Lucia upon my birth, this instantly triggered my return to the past.

As a little boy growing up in St. Lucia, I had never thought to ask about the pair of white baby boots with silver bells fastened to white laces that seemed as permanent a fixture as our furniture. It was much more than a pair of boots. They seemed multi-purpose and nomadic, doubling up as our goal posts when we played football in the yard or in the kitchen, at times playing the part of the ball. The two little boots served as our wickets when we played cricket, at other times, the ball. Sometimes, from a corner of the room, lonely and abandoned, the pair of boots simply sat there as we played marbles, or rounders, or arm-wrestled, or listened to scary stories of boloms roaming the woods.

It had never occurred to me to question how the little boots moved about from room to room, as though they were one of us. Sometimes we spotted one of them or both lying outside in the yard next to the fowl coop, or the pit latrine, or on the river bank, or at the bottom of the hill as we slid down the steep slope on stems of trimmed coconut branches – only to find that next morning, like obedient pets, the boots lay on the floor at our feet as we munched our breakfast. It never occurred to me to ask about their origins – whose were they? Where did they come from? It never occurred to me that the white baby boots with silver bells had an owner – that I was the owner – my first and only gift from my paternal grandparents in Barbados.

It was with a twinge of sadness that I vaguely recalled packing away the tattered pair of boots into the old trunk destined for the rubbish dump as we moved from LaClery to Morne-du-Don, after the devastation of Hurricane Allen.

My grandmother's eyes hardly left my face as she spoke. I wondered what private thoughts occupied the deepest recesses of her mind. When at one point, standing over and behind me she casually ran a warm hand through my hair, her eyes studying me closely, I didn't have to guess what she was thinking. She was feeling for the texture of my hair. Was it hard or soft? How hard, how soft? The softer the more pedigree – the closer to one's European heritage. It wasn't as if she had consciously considered these questions; it was more instinctive, subconscious, like the way a seamstress inspected fabric to determine its ilk. It was simply something West Indians did, though most resorted to inspecting with their eyes, rather than with their hands. But she was my granny . . . it was her right.

I hadn't the slightest clue about her verdict.

As the afternoon progressed, it felt as though some unspoken agreement had been sworn between the three of us. My grandmother would tell all – all that we needed to know; that was her job. Susanna and I would listen, ask questions; that was our job. Like perfect courtiers, we played our roles, observing unspoken rules of discretion, respect, the need to maintain a pleasant, courteous atmosphere; no guilt trips, no subtle attacks, no finger-pointing.

For me, observing the rules came naturally, for it was nothing but pure joy that I felt, and, it seemed, so did Susanna, who never stopped holding my hand and smiling at her grandmother-in-law.

The tour through the well-worn family album was like sitting through an expertly narrated documentary. I watched and listened, dumbfounded not just by the stories behind the images, but by the images themselves. Images of the man who bore such striking resemblance to me – or was it the other way around?

Yet another uncanny feeling swept through my bones. It was as if we were reviewing the life of my twin; a twin separated at birth; something straight out of Hollywood.

Sitting back, my eyes riveted onto what seemed the photograph page of an old passport. It bore the face of a young man. I felt Susanna's grip tighten as I heard that now familiar chant, in a quick intense whisper: "Rudy, that's you!"

Peering closely, I could barely make out the faded letters stamped across Rodney's youthful, unsmiling face – 31st August 1963. My mind wandered. *31st August 1963.* A mere two months before seventeen-year-old Rosemary would have been rushed to Victoria Hospital, where she would have lain on the narrow bed in the delivery room, writhing, snivelling, cursing the man who, for the second time, had been responsible for inflicting upon her such excruciating pain. I wondered how it was for her. Would she have preferred Rodney at her side, or was she at all comforted that he had made the sacrifice and trekked the four thousand miles across the Atlantic to make a way for his young family? Was she . . . ?

The vibrant crowing of a rooster resounded from outside, rousing my mind back to the present. My grandmother's lips were still moving – something about Rodney's days in the British army. Susanna's grip on my arm was tight and warm.

Another page. My eyes focused on the black and white picture of the young man dressed in military fatigues as he stood in what seemed a snow-covered field; a young man – a spitting image of a youthful me. Like the much theorized extrasensory perception between twins, Rodney's unsmiling face, his poise, the sad look in his eyes, instantly told me that he was deep in thought, that he was miserable, that he preferred to be elsewhere. Anywhere but the cold, wintry landscape. Was he longing for the warmth of the Caribbean? Perhaps he was thinking of Rosemary, or his two infant children, or both. Perhaps . . . perhaps.

Susanna flipped the page. My eyes saw the image of a middle-aged man, dressed in jeans and a tight-fitting white tee-shirt. He was bending over a light-skinned little boy in red jersey and brown shorts. Caution was written all over Rodney's face as he took great care holding onto the handlebar, steadying the little boy's tricycle.

"This is Semeon," the old lady's voice said with a hint of pride. "He was born in 1983."

1983, I heard myself thinking. 1983 . . . that was the year that I had graduated from the SDA Academy, the year that my little brother had been born. Rodney would have been forty. I wonder . . .

I banished the thought.

Another page, another picture. My eyes zeroed in on an older Rodney, apparently in his mid-forties. Not bad-looking for his age. Perhaps there was hope yet for me. The clearly proud father and husband posed with his two sons and beautiful wife with a British Airways jet in the background, and an unfocused image of an overweight white woman ascending the aircraft's steep metal stairs.

"They were on their way back to England after spending six weeks with me in Barbados," said my grandmother, casually.

Just a thirty-five minute flight from St. Lucia, my mind insisted on reminding me. Immediately, I dispelled the thought. I had no intention of breaching our unspoken contract.

Overleaf, I studied the faded picture of a pensive-looking old man seated alone in a balcony. We listened to the old lady speaking with longing of her husband who, after a prolonged illness, had passed on the year before. Together, the couple had lived in the same spot for over sixty years. The original wooden house where Rodney had spent his youth had been rebuilt into the concrete structure in which we now sat.

The aroma of roasting coffee drifted in from outside as my mind again strayed. I wondered how it would have been growing up in Barbados. What sort of relationship would I have had with my grandfather? If only I had got in touch with Rodney earlier, perhaps I would have met the old man . . .

When we heard the forceful knock on the door, our necks craned in unison. My grandmother hoisted herself up from the sofa and walked slowly but steadily towards the entrance. She returned with a large, cheerful-looking brown-skinned, middle-aged man on her heels. She introduced Susanna and me to Rodney's boyhood friend.

"No need to introduce me to this young man here," said the heavyset man jovially, his Barbadian accent strong.

"I know he . . . he's a clone of Rodney when he were young. I see when he pull up in de taxi. Yes, I see he from my house over there across the road." He pointed over his shoulder, towards the road, his words coming in quick bursts. "And when he get out de car I thought I was dreaming. Cor blimey! The way he walk, how he look, he height, he mannerisms . . . I tell you, he is a clone of Rodney. Just a little lighter complexion . . . that is all."

He fixed his gaze on my smiling face and with a note of finality, said, "Boy, you is a picture of you Dad. You don't need no damn DNA test!"

He proved a source of entertaining stories; stories about Rodney's boyhood, and about my family. He asked about my Aunt Sheila, who, he said, had taught the teenagers in Grazettes to dance; about Rosemary's mother, who seemed a really nice, quiet lady.

He did not ask about Rosemary.

When, after forty-five minutes or so of sheer entertainment, Rodney's friend glanced at my watch then rose to announce his departure, somehow I felt a twinge of sadness. In a way I felt I had just experienced part of my father's boyhood, and I found myself longing for more.

It wasn't long after that that Susanna and I were heading out through the front door, kissing and hugging my grandmother, going towards the taxi that awaited us outside.

CHAPTER 34

The London Eye had originally been conceived as a commemorative structure to celebrate the new millennium. Towering five hundred feet, the world's largest observation wheel has thirty-two capsules each capable of carrying up to twenty-five people. It provides visitors with a breathtaking birds-eye view of up to twenty-five miles across the city. Not only has the Eye transformed London's skyline, but it has pulled off arguably the biggest coup d'état in UK tourism history. The once dominant Big Ben, Tower Bridge, and St. Paul's Cathedral now bow to the undisputed champion of UK tourist landmarks.

From our room on the ninth floor at London's Novotel hotel, Susanna and I had a clear view of the towering giant in the distance. But this time around we wouldn't be among its four million annual visitors. We had other preoccupations.

The Eye was farthest from my mind as I flicked a nervous glance at my watch. We had been waiting in the hotel lobby for the past ten minutes, and with a bit more anxiety than we cared to let on.

Then I caught sight of the tall, light-skinned man who pushed his way through the revolving door.

There was no mistaking him.

My pulse was leaping. Susanna was beaming.

Looking sharp in his charcoal-grey business suit, briefcase in hand, he stood in front of the door, his bespectacled eyes darting nervously around the bustling lobby. When his searching eyes found our frantic waves from our seats around the coffee table on the raised platform left of the entrance, Rodney broke into a nervous half smile.

His smile lingered as he strode towards us. Feeling an upwelling of excitement, it dawned on me that I was staring at my future – catching a glimpse of how a late-fifties me would look. Just a shade over my six feet, only slightly darker than me, Rodney's broad-shouldered physique, his vertical posture, his military stride, his soft-featured face, was all me; an older me with thinning, greying hair.

I hadn't decided whether or not I was happy with the older me by the time I realized that my father was standing there, smiling down at us.

Feeling a wave of nervous excitement washing over me, our faces wreathed in smiles, Susanna and I hurriedly rose to greet him. As we shook hands he pulled me gently into a slight hug; a brief, manly embrace. He'd already planted a kiss on Susanna's cheek by the time I'd had the chance to introduce the two.

I invited him to join us around the coffee table.

For a long moment, no one spoke as we sat in our alcove next to the glass partition.

Then Rodney and I both tried to speak at once.

"So how are you . . ." I said.

"How are things . . ." said Rodney.

We paused, smiling off our feeble attempt to break the ice.

"Sorry, please go ahead," I said, gesturing.

"No, you."

"I insist."

Rodney raised his hand in mock surrender, smiling.

"I'm really happy to finally meet you and your beautiful wife, Rudy."

"We're pleased to meet you too," said Susanna and I in unison. "Finally," I added.

He fished a white handkerchief from his inside jacket pocket and dabbed the beads of sweat forming on his forehead and nose. "You can tell how nervous I am . . . right?"

I smiled. "We're all nervous. Don't worry about it, man. That's perfectly natural."

My father's lips quivered as he spoke. "For a moment, as I walked into the lobby and didn't see you, I thought that perhaps you might have changed your mind."

I put a slight frown on my face as he pocketed the handkerchief. "Really? We wouldn't do that. After all, I've been looking forward to this moment all my life, and I'm not about to get cold feet now."

Rodney nodded. "That's good to hear."

Then I saw his eyes wandering across the lobby, a wicked little smile prancing about his lips. "You seem to have a lot of style, Rudy."

I raised my eyebrows, smiling. "Style?"

Susanna sat next to me, her eyes studying Rodney's face as if trying to work out something that I sensed had something to do with me. Perhaps she was wondering whether I too was destined to lose one of my premolars in later years.

Rodney began to clarify his words. "I mean . . . your choice of hotel . . . it's really opulent . . . I can see you're a man of fine taste." Beaming, like a bashful schoolboy, he gestured towards the elegant lobby.

"Actually, this is my favourite hotel in London," I said. "This is where I stay whenever I come over. It's new and modern and I kinda like that. And when I like something, I tend to stick with it."

For some reason that escaped me, an embarrassed flush began to surge through Rodney's cheeks, and neck. "Must be very expensive," he gushed.

I made light of the comment, wanting to change the subject.

His smile persisting, he ran his eyes over the black jacket I wore over black slacks, before shifting his gaze to Susanna's black blazer and knee-length skirt. "I love your jacket . . . you both look really debonair. You seem to have done very, very well for yourselves."

"You look cool as well, in your business suit," I muttered, privately amused by the man's preoccupation with things material.

"Thanks. I look forward to not having to wear these suits any more when I retire, some time next year."

"I don't blame you. I'm hoping to retire early at some point myself in the not-too-distant future."

Susanna's gaze was fixed on Rodney's face, her expression somewhat quizzical. "Rodney, it feels really strange sitting here and watching the two of you, father and son. I never thought I would ever get to meet Rudy's father. This is so surreal."

She paused a moment, and shook her head, fascinated. "And the two of you look so much alike."

Rodney's smile was awkward. He adjusted his silk tie, again pulled out his handkerchief, and began dabbing at the little beads of sweat that seemed to have mysteriously reappeared on his forehead and nose.

Somehow, eyeing my father more closely, I found myself thinking that Rodney would look years younger were he to shave off his thinning, greying hair. I wondered how I'd look with a cleanly shaven head. Then my mind took on his thick-rimmed glasses. *Hadn't the man heard of contact lenses?*

Susanna's voice roused me from my thoughts. Something about not being able to fathom how my mother's and father's eyes were so much alike.

For the ensuing few minutes, our conversation

continued in that strangely desultory manner. Then a tall Pakistani waiter in a smart blue uniform came and took our drinks order. Moments later he returned with a tray bearing Susanna's fruit punch, Rodney's Screw Driver, and my Bloody Mary.

No sooner had we picked up the cold drinks off the coffee table in front of us than I found myself studying Rodney's body language. Left leg crossed over right knee, left elbows propped up over the back of the sofa, he leaned back, reflectively swirling the drink in his glass. Then I heard Susanna's intrigued voice commenting that I sat in remarkably the same manner, swirling my drink the very same way.

My father's face turned a brighter shade of red as we both flashed awkward smiles, and quickly changed our pose.

After an awkward beat of silence, I heard Rodney's voice explaining that he'd stayed up all night tracking the progress of our flight across the Atlantic on Virgin's website. That provoked a little chuckle from me, for I'd never thought he would have displayed the mannerisms of a doting father.

From there, it was smooth sailing, the conversation drifting easily along with a nice, even rhythm.

About this and that we spoke. Like a private detective, Rodney dug up information on my career and on Susanna's; how, when, and where we'd met; our plans for the future, not least when we planned to have children. Susanna and I, in turn, seemed intent on writing the man's biography. We quizzed him on everything: growing up in Barbados; his time in St. Lucia; life in England – the full works.

We listened quietly as he explained that Rosemary was barely seventeen when she had given birth to my sister in Barbados. After Roslyn's birth, Rosemary's blind father had summoned the family back to St. Lucia. Rodney had followed afterwards, and then spent the next six months job-hunting. He'd had his sights set on joining the Royal St. Lucian Police Force, but although he'd supplied all the requested documents nothing came out of it. Rosemary's father had accompanied him to an interview at M&C, a company with fingers in a good many commercial pies on the island, but the interview proved fruitless. Rosemary was already six months pregnant with me when Rodney decided that the family's best hope was for him to go to the UK, and to send for his fiancé and children once he'd settled down in a good job. He did get the job, but the rest wasn't meant to be. He'd made some mistakes.

Sensing his discomfort, we veered him onto safer ground. Susanna seemed pleased to hear that other than having high blood-pressure, my father was in perfect health.

I all but fell off my seat when Rodney mentioned that he'd named me after his favourite poet – Rudyard Kipling, the British writer who'd also written my favourite poem – 'If'. I marvelled that I'd had to wait thirty-eight years to find that out.

I also marvelled at the coincidence. I wondered whether Rodney knew of Kipling's imperialist views.

Disappointment creased Rodney's face when I pointed out that the names that had made their way onto my birth certificates were Reedy and Radney, on account of transcription errors.

I soon realized that I felt towards Rodney a little more kinship than I'd felt towards my mother when I had met her that wintry day in Milton Keynes. Meeting my father was more than meeting a long-lost friend. I couldn't quite put a finger on why I felt different towards Rodney. Perhaps it had something to do with our physical resemblance to each other. Perhaps, to my shame, it was down to the fact that the man had made something of himself, that he had achieved some degree of success. I wasn't sure. But yes. Years ago I could have seen this man as my father.

As my eyes followed, and my ears tuned in to the man with the anglicized Barbadian accent who, for so many years, had been more elusive than even the Scarlet Pimpernel, a myriad of thoughts paraded across my mind. I recalled the bitterly cold hours I'd spent standing in smelly phone booths dialling hundreds of listings under R. Greenidge. I recalled the pile of letters I'd written to the Inland Revenue, the Department of Health and Social Security and London Transport – all in the vain attempt to track down the living, breathing man now sitting right there before me.

Vaguely, I recalled searching faces of men as I rode the buses and the underground, and stalked up and down the streets of London. Those had been days of desperation, days when I faced potential destitution, homelessness, ruin. I had needed help back then. As a last resort, I'd searched hopelessly for the father I wasn't meant to find until twenty years later.

Now, as I sat back in my seat, legs crossed, gazing at my father, listening to him, no greater feeling could I have than the feeling that I now felt. It was the same feeling Billie Holiday must have felt when she crooned the classic: 'God Bless the Child that's got his Own'. It was this sort of feeling that consumed me. The feeling that I needed not a thing from the man.

CHAPTER 35

The next week I was back at my desk.

Late that Thursday evening, I sat back, reminiscing on the success of our UK trip. Not only had I met my father but also I'd had a wonderful time mingling with his family over a sumptuous meal at his home. The man had done well for himself, and his family were perhaps the greater part of his success. He'd done a good job bringing up his two sons and daughter from his previous marriage. No doubt the woman behind him, his lovely wife, who'd forgiven his sins of a previous life, had contributed immensely to his success.

Yes. Rodney was a happy man that Sunday afternoon when the two sides of his family met in complete harmony. He'd played an excellent host to his five children and only grandchild, Roslyn's sixteen-year-old daughter.

But now as I sat alone in my office, the thought that was uppermost in my mind was something I'd said to Rodney when the entire family had again sat together over dinner, this time at the Novotel. Rodney had asked about my next career move. My next move, I'd said, was a move back to St. Lucia, to sit in the general manager's chair.

I'd made that statement without much prior thought. But little did I suspect then that chaotic events brewing in Rodney's birthplace, would present me the opportunity to make my ambition a reality much sooner than I'd expected.

When the Barbadian authorities had finally given C&W the go-ahead to merge its disparate companies on the island, it was a precondition, unspoken or otherwise, that a Barbadian should remain at the helm of the merged entity. Nothing surprising there, for, unlike many Caribbean islands, Barbados had a long-standing tradition of a local boy running the C&W show.

It came as a seismic shock when the company suddenly announced that it had appointed an American CEO to manage its operations in Barbados. Fiercely proud and patriotic, the Barbadian government and people kicked up a storm. It didn't help C&W's cause that it hadn't even applied for a work permit ahead of its announcement. The company had been rude and disrespectful to the sovereign nation of Barbados and to its people. That was the talk on the streets – and in the corridors of power – in the tiny Caribbean island.

It seemed to many that C&W, rooted in a colonial past, had learned very little about Barbados's psyche as a nation, as a government, as a people. Either that, or C&W had taken leave of its senses. Despite its status as 'Little Britain', Barbados, it seemed, had attained a level of national pride and cohesion that enabled the small nation to remain the true master of its destiny – a factor, no doubt, contributing to its designation as a developed country in a developing region, and to its unofficial designation as the most successful black country on the planet.

C&W would find no loophole to crawl out of this time.

And it was in the midst of this crisis that I saw the opportunity that presented itself.

I had long ago learned a simple truth about getting the things that I desired: that the first step is to ask for it.

When I picked up the phone and placed a call to C&W's Eastern Caribbean CEO, it wasn't a favour that I sought. The company had found itself in hot water. What I offered, was a way out of not just the hot water but the entire kitchen. Why not transfer Don Austin, the Barbadian running C&W St. Lucia, back to his homeland to lead the local company? At the same time, I'd be more than happy to replace Don as the head of C&W St. Lucia. Two birds, one stone. And my performance in Grenada spoke of my ability to make a success of St. Lucia, I put in as modestly as I could.

When, two weeks later, my personal assistant's

voice over the speakerphone informed me that the CEO was on the line to me, I braced myself. After the two or three-minute conversation, during which my fingers tugged nervously at my goatee, I put the telephone down, ran a weary hand through my hair, glanced down at Susanna's picture on my desk, and punched the air energetically, bellowing, "Yes! *Yes! Yes!*"

In an uncharacteristic burst of sheer glee, I whirled myself around in the swivel chair until the room too, had begun spinning. It was several moments before my gleaming eyes picked up the dim image of someone standing in the doorway. The expression on the employee's face was that of one who had just witnessed the act of a man who'd gone stark raving mad.

CHAPTER 36

'Be careful what you ask for,' the ancient wisdom says, 'for you might just get it.'

When in September 2002 I became the first local to head C&W St. Lucia in its over one-hundred-and-thirty year history, I got what I'd asked for.

And I got a lot more that I *hadn't* asked for.

I was mostly happy about what I'd got.

I was happy when television and radio personality Claudius Francis named me St. Lucia's Entrepreneur of the Year for 2003.

I was happy when London appointed me Chairman of the Board of Directors of C&W Grenada Ltd.

I was happy, also, when C&W appointed me to represent the group on the Board of Telecommunications Services of Trinidad and Tobago Ltd, in which C&W had a minority interest.

My happiness, it seemed, was endless.

I was happy when I received a grant of share options – a potential fortune – of 100,000 C&W shares.

I was happy when London chose not only to feature St.Lucia's competitive strategy in the C&W Group 2004 Annual Review, but also to depict on the front cover, a breathtaking image of St. Lucia's twin peaks, the majestic Pitons, a World Heritage site.

I was happy when I was appointed to the Board of St. Lucia's Chamber of Commerce, Industry and Agriculture.

Yes. The little boy from LaClery, from St. Lucia, from the Caribbean – had done well. His had been a Caribbean tale worth telling. His dreams, his hopes, his aspirations had been more than fulfilled.

I had followed the rules. I had stuck with my positive thinking principles. And by the sweat of my brow I had eaten much more than just a piece of bread.

Yes. I was happy.

But I wasn't happy when a certain Englishman took up residence in my back yard. Nor was I happy when, soon after, I became the subject of scalding rumours that began to spread like a wave of acid across the island. Everywhere. Rumours. Rumours of my imminent demise.

My future was going to be nothing like my past.

RUDY GURLEY

PROUDLY PRESENTS

the sequel to A Caribbean Tale

SENT FROM OVERSEAS

available in paperback
in 2007